DORDT INFORMATION SERVICES
3 6520 0050830 W
W9-BUF-528

Christhard Mahrenholz

THE CALCULATION OF ORGAN PIPE SCALES

from the middle ages to the mid-nineteenth century

Translated by
Andrew H. Williams

Positif Press, Oxford 1975

2931355

Originally published by Bärenreiter-Verlag Kassel, Basel, Paris, London, New York
© Bärenreiter-Verlag Karl Vötterle KG Kassel und Basel 1968

Christhard Mahrenholz

DIE BERECHNUNG DER ORGELPFEIFENMENSUREN
vom Mittelalter bis zur Mitte des 19. Jahrhunderts

This translation © 1975 A. H. Williams and Positif Press, Oxford.
Printed by B. H. Blackwell in the City of Oxford
Published 1975 by Positif Press, 130 Southfield Road, Oxford OX4 1PA

ISBN 0 9503892 2 6

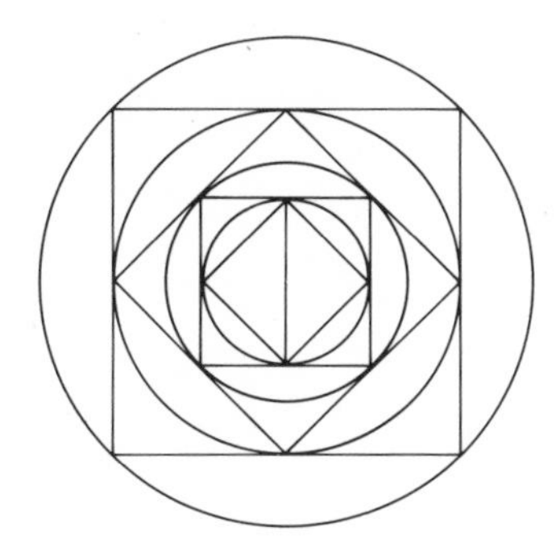

Contents

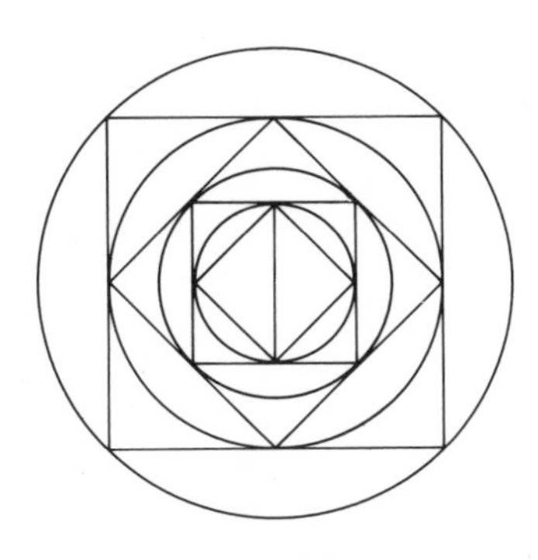

Introduction

At the 1926 Freiburg German Organ Congress a lively discussion arose about whether the old master organ-builders kept strictly to "sacred numbers" in calculating organ scales or had the full freedom of their "artistic intuition."[1] The Congress director, W. Gurlitt indicated that an answer to the problem raised was urgently needed. An attempt at such an answer is presented in this study.

Originally it was intended to bring together and evaluate systematically as fully as possible everything supplied by the sources on the question of organ scaling in the widest sense. It became more and more apparent that the resultant weighty tome would present real problems, especially in the field of practical application of the scaling rules thus discovered. So all the material relating to actual scaling history was withdrawn and the theme restricted to the history of scaling calculation, which anyway contains the key to whatever can be found or learnt in scaling history. In order to prevent this account from becoming unwieldy I have confined myself to showing the various types in the history of organ-building for the scaling of pipe length (part I) and pipe width (part II), without attempting to draw exhaustively on the source material or to extend the survey to flue, chest and wind or other scales. It will already become clear that the art of organ-building in earlier times did not create its masterpieces without a critical linking to the unchanging laws of sound. It is my wish that the present work, which covers fresh ground for wind instruments, may give an impulse to research of the same kind in other areas of organology. In my opinion particular questions in the history of musical instruments will not find a satisfactory answer until the complex entered into here has light shed upon it.

In the discussion at Freiburg it was by no means only a question of how the old masters saw and respected the following of formulae and rules under question; in the background there was implicit far more an attempt to come to terms with the scaling of organs in the future and its principles. The debate on variable scales has meanwhile rightly died down and the whole discussion has lost the keenness of an immediate concern, but the question itself still remains the same; can creative intuition in organ-building offer anything healthy and valuable without the most exact knowledge of acoustical laws and a voluntary subjection to rules that are perhaps uncomfortable now and then, which we may know and evaluate imperfectly, but which can be beneficial to the design of an organ? I believe that this study, although – or because – it is only historically oriented can also offer something towards answering this question.

---

[1] Cf. my statements in discussion given in the report of the Freiburg Organ Congress (Augsburg 1929), p. 57: "The expositions of Dr Walcker and H. H. Jahnn showed encouraging agreement on a decisive point significant for organ-building, i.e. a complete renunciation of Töpfer's constant scales and the recognition and recommendation of variable scales. Only one question was answered differently by both speakers. While H. H. Jahnn explains the presence of variable scales in the old masters from the knowledge of the "sacred numbers" 3,5 and 7 lost to us today, and wishes to support the application of variable scales today by a conscious incorporation of values of "strength, fullness and sharpness," which can be grasped by the mind and calculation, with the help of the exact physical formulae, Dr Walcker considers variable scales with the old as well as modern masters to be values apart from calculation and the mathematically fixable, proceeding from the artistic intuition of a given master. The answer to the question, which view is right in relation to the 16th and 17th centuries must, as Professor Gurlitt says, be left to scientific research and chance (e.g. the discovery of some long unknown music treatise). On the other hand the question concerning the present is of particular importance to us today because of its consequences. For if the application of variable scales, recognised by both speakers as the only correct ones, is dependent on artistic intuition, and if such intuition, which cannot be learnt, is an essential requisite for the profession of organ-builder, every organ-builder would have to be an artist in this respect. But the neglect of variable scales by surely worthy masters in the last century proves the opposite. This whole complex of questions still needs thorough investigation"

I then soon expected to publish a work on this subject, which had already long concerned me. The greater part of the following treatise was ready in 1928 in manuscript as part of my work on organ registers (Kassel, 1930), ready for printing, but had to be withdrawn, so as not to make the book too extensive. Professional duties later hindered completion of the work, so that my consent given in Freiburg can only now be acquitted, over a decade later.

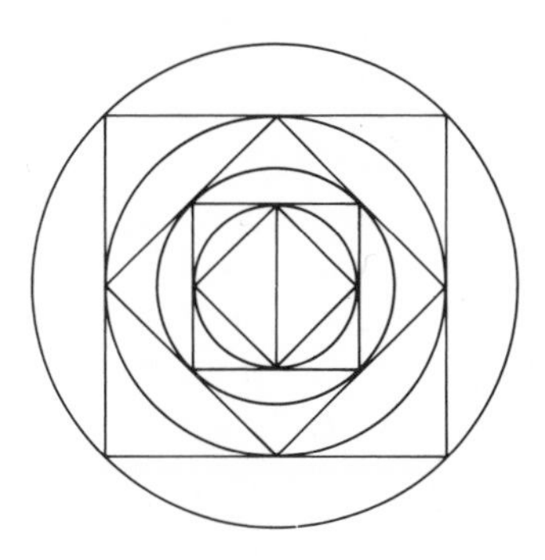

I Pipe Length

1

As long as the width of pipes remained the same throughout the scale (see p. 31), i.e. to about the thirteenth century, the interest of the student of organ-building theory has been directed almost exclusively to questions of pipe length. An account and critical analysis of literary evidence from this period is difficult because it extends over nearly 4 centuries, but especially since it is almost impossible to date the individual sources and thus arrange the material chronologically. A large part of the sources have come down to us with particular names attached. It can often be demonstrated, however, that the names have either been added later or that the author concerned transcribed his material more or less word for word from earlier sources. Besides, as H. Riemann has already pointed out,[2] information about organ-building was often written up by a later hand on blank or partially filled pages or as appendices to treatises having nothing to do with the subject of organ-building.[3]

Contradictions and inconsistencies in accounts given under the name of a particular author are thus the order of the day.[4] Discerning this

---

[2] Orgelbau im frühen Mittelalter (Allgemeine Musikalische Zeitung, XIV, 1879, p.65ff; later also given in : Preludien und Studien II, p.190ff).

[3] M. Gerbert (Scriptores ecclesiastici de musica sacra potissimum, St Blasien, 1784, 3 vols) says the same for one case (vol. 1, p.325a, observation b).

[4] I give here only the 6 scale prescriptions, following one another, contained in the chapter "De Mensuris organicarum fistularum"of Hucbald's Musica (Gerbert I, 147ff). It must also be observed that in such cases the prescriptions pre-supposed different scales for the keyboard (see below, p. 13), as well as various methods of calculation. It is precisely this which makes it unlikely that one author is responsible.

state of affairs is made the more difficult because such interpolations are not simply joined to the existing text; they are disguised by extensive additions or even so reworked to suit the context, that it is only possible to distinguish the original layer with certainty if this has come down to us by some chance in another place and context.[5]

In order not to allow the account given later to become too extended, for the reasons given above, I provide first a summary of tracts up to the twelfth century concerning organ pipe scales, limited to printed material available and sources offering something of importance on the question of length or width scale.[6]

1) *Prima quantaecumque quantitatis . . . ascribed to Hucbald (Gerbert, loc. cit. I, 148a).*
2) *Prima per octavam metiatur . . ., named as by Hucbald (Gerbert I, 147b)*
3) *In primo diapason: E habet (totum) F . . . given as by a) Hucbald (Gerbert I,121f)*[7]*, b) Bernelinus (Gerbert I, 329b).*
4) *Mensura fistularum et monochordi. Bernelinus is given as author (Gerbert I, 314ff). The relevant section extends to p.321.*
5) *Prima fistula in VIII divisa . . . (Cod. Paul. Lips. 1493 fol. 61a, new edition in: H. Riemann, Studien zur Geschichte der Notenschrift, Leipzig, 1878, p. 301).*
6) *Mensuram et ordinem instrumenti organici . . . from the Berne anon (Codex Bernensis Martiani Capellae 56b, printed in: Schubiger, Musikal. Spicilegien, p. 82 and H. Riemann, Studien zur Geschichte der Notenschrift, p.300).*
7) *Monitum ad semitonium inveniendum. A summa quacunque locata . . . This account is given twice in the Musica of Bernelinus (Gerbert I, 325b and I,330a).*
8) *Organicae dispositionis mensura. Ex A suspende primum . . . ascribed to Aribo Scholasticus (Gerbert II, 224b).*
9) *Si fistulae aequalis grossitudinis fuerint . . . (Paris Bibl. nat. MS lat. 12949 bl.43a, saec. IX, printed in: E.Buhle, die musikalischen Instrumente in den Miniaturen . . . I, p.104f; also given in an almost identical version attached to the name of Gerlandus (Gerbert II, 277), and as part (Item de fistulis) in the Berne Codex organ-building treatise and the Einsiedeln MS 319 (Schubinger, op. cit., p.84).*

---

[5] The "mensura fistularum et monochordi" by Bernelinus (Gerbert I, 314ff) raises particularly difficult problems here.

[6] For an explanation of the arrangement chosen, see p.26f below.

[7] A number of errors are corrected in the errata found in Gerbert.

Sources 10 and 11, together with 9, derive from a common source, but treat the semitone and whole tone differently and are therefore given separately.

10) Si fistulae aequalis grossitudinis fuerint . . . ascribed to Hucbald (Gerbert I,148b).

11) Si fistulae aequalis grossitudinis erunt . . . probably by Bernelinus (Gerbert I, 329a).

12) Data igitur primae vel minori fistulae, ascribed to Eberhard of Freising (Gerbert II, 280b).

13) Data igitur primae vel minori fistulae . . . given in the Musica of Hucbald (Gerbert I, 148a).

14) Data igitur primae vel minori fistulae . . . preserved under the name of Bernelinus (Gerbert I,322b). 12-14 derive from a common source; 12 offers the oldest text.

15) Sicut in monochordo . . . with a table of pipe lenths given in the treatise of Bernelinus (Gerbert I,323b-325a).

16) Prima habeat octies suum diametrum . . ., shown as originating with Hucbald (Gerbert I, 147b).

17) Nova fistularum mensura quae remittitur . . . given in the Musica of Aribo Scholasticus as due to Wilhelm of Hirsau, d.1091, (Gerbert 11, 223a)[8]*.*

18) In metiendis organorum fistulis . . . ascribed to Eberhard of Freising (Gerbert II,280b). The main section, beginning with the sentence Primae igitur (or: ergo) fistulae quantitas . . . is almost exactly the same as in 17 and 18.

19) Si tonum quaeris . . . given under Hucbald's name (Gerbert I, 148a) and Bernelinus (Gerbert 1,328a); the latter has two scribal errors, to be corrected in accordance with Gerbert I. 148a).

20) Aribunculina[9] *fistularum mensura . . . ascribed to Aribo Scholasticus (Gerbert II, 224a).*

21) Sîd tû nû bechénêst, uuîo âlle . . . in Notker's hand (probably Notker Labeo, d. 1022). Gerbert's version I,101 has been superseded by Paul Piper's edition, Die Schriften Notkers . . . I,857)[10]*.*

22) Fac tibi fistulam . . . anon (Gerbert II, 283)

23) Cognita omnia consonantia . . . also anon (Gerbert II,287a).

---

[8] But there is no question here of a special flute scale or an explanation of the arrangement of this flute as Hans Müller, Die Musik Wilhelms von Hirschau, Frankfurt 1883, says.

[9] Given as "Aribonis" in Gerbert.

[10] This section has been reprinted by J. Schmidt-Görg in the Kirchenmusikalisches Jahrburch 1932, p.58ff.

24) *Octavam partem diametri . . . ascribed to Gerlandus (Gerbert II, 278a).*
25) *Antiqua fistularum mensura quae intenditur . . . given as by Aribo Scholasticus (Gerbert II,222a).*
26) *Mensarum fistularum dicturi . . . ascribed to Eberhard of Freising (Gerbert II, 279). The main section, beginning Primam fistulam tantae longtitudinis . . . is almost the same in 25 and 26. It re-appears more or less word for word in:*
27) *Primam fistulam quam longam . . . anon (Gerbert II, 283b).*
28) *Igitur verbi gratia . . . from the Musica of Bernelinus (Gerbert I, 321a).*
29) *Igitur ut breviter . . . also by Bernelinus (Gerbert I, 325a).*

2

The early theorists give no generally valid formulae for calculating pipe length. Instead they offer precise calculations for direct practical use, using a given standard pipe as a basis. All the source material can be divided into two clearly distinct parts, according to whether the highest pipe in the series (as in the majority of sources) or the lowest (in the more recent ones) is taken as standard. This fact must be kept in view throughout the following descriptions. In the explanations of pipe length calculation nearly all the theorists take as their starting point the fact (demonstrated in practice) that the divisions of the monochord can be directly applied to organ pipe lengths, and that the relationships of string length to pitch produced on the monochord are also valid for pipe lengths.[11] This explains why the relevant sections in the sources may have headings such as: Mensura fistularum et organorum" (Gerbert I, 329b) or similar.

Thus the first group of sources, covering nos 1-8, follows the rules valid for the monochord exclusively in establishing pipe length. Prescriptions 1-4 take the smallest pipe as standard and determine the length of the whole tone (calculated from the standard pipe) as $\frac{9}{8}$, the fourth as $\frac{4}{3}$, the fifth as $\frac{3}{2}$, the octave as 2, etc., following the Pythagorean scale, as do all the ancient scale prescriptions.[12] 4 calculates the intervals using "differences",[13] gives a monochord table covering 10 octaves and adds a 2-octave pipe length table (Gerbert I,

---

[11] i.e. pipe lengths are related to each in a reciprocal ratio of vibration figures.

[12] More details on the calculations in the individual tracts are reproduced below in another context (p. 15).

[13] see below, p. 23.

321). 7 was probably only intended as a supplement to scale treatises already in existence; hence it is restricted to the calculation of the Pythagorean semitone ($=\frac{256}{243}$), the minor third ($=\frac{32}{27}$), the major third ($=\frac{81}{64}$) and the apotome or chromatic semitone ($=\frac{80128}{75816}=\frac{10016}{9477}$).[14] Treatises 5 and 6 take the largest pipe as standard; 6 thus calculates the major second as $\frac{8}{9}$, octave as $\frac{1}{2}$, etc. 5 has a rather unusual sequence, with the second always given as $\frac{7}{8}$ instead of $\frac{8}{9}$. I suggest[15] that here we have one of the earliest attempts to take the largest pipe as standard, keeping the division into eighths normal when using the smallest pipe , i.e. $1-\frac{1}{8}$, instead of $1+\frac{1}{8}$.[16] 8 calculates the pipes by means of the circle of fifths and fourths; from C, F is reached by means of the upper fourth, G from the use of the upper fifth. From G the lower fourth is D, A the upper fifth from D, etc. When figures are not given explicitly, a fifth value of $\frac{2}{3}$ and a fourth of $\frac{3}{4}$ are assumed.

Calculation of pipe length using the monochord is also applied in the second group, including treatises 9-20. All these sources take the smallest pipe as their standard. Sources 9-11 are limited to giving prescriptions for calculating the semitone, whole tone, fourth, fifth, octave and double octave. Sources 12-14 are limited still more to the whole tone, fourth, fifth and octave.[17] Not until 15 are complete series extending

---

[14] A distinction is made in the Pythagorean system between the limma, the true diatonic semitone ($=\frac{256}{243}$) and the apotome, the chromatic semitone. The value of the apotome is obtained by subtracting the limma from the whole tone; the result is $\frac{9}{8}\cdot\frac{243}{256}=\frac{2187}{2048}$. The value given above in the text for 7 ($\frac{10016}{9477}$) is too small relative to the normal value.

[15] I do not agree with Buhle's view (op.cit., p.91) that mouth correction is already involved here. The fourth is correctly given as $\frac{3}{4}$ without mouth correction, and similarly the octave as $\frac{1}{2}$.

[16] The series arrived at in this way ($1, \frac{7}{8}, \frac{49}{64}, \frac{3}{4}, \frac{21}{32}, \frac{147}{256}, \frac{1029}{2048}, \frac{1}{2}$) gives a five-step scale, since $\frac{49}{64}$ and $\frac{3}{4}$ as well as $\frac{1029}{2048}$ and $\frac{1}{2}$ can be treated as almost the same, such as is known in Java as slendro. Cf. J.P. Land in the Vierteljahrschrift für Musikwissenschaft, vol. V, 1889, p. 193f. I thank Erich Thienhaus for this information. See also table II, p. 17

[17] The theoretical pipe lengths (without mouth correction, see below) are given in sources 9-14 as follows, with the length of the shortest pipe, used as standard, given as 1:

Fundamental:	1
semitone	$\frac{17}{16}$ (inexact reduction of $\frac{256}{243}$)
whole tone	$\frac{9}{8}$
fourth	$\frac{4}{3}$
fifth	$\frac{3}{2}$
octave	2
double octave	4

Semitone and double octave are not given in 12-14, nor fourth in 11, or whole tone

over one or two octaves given, as in the first group. In this group we find that pipe length is not only calculated according to the monochord; an additional value is also given for every pipe length, usually as part of the diameter (d), e.g:

fourth = $\frac{4}{3} + \frac{1}{3}$d
fifth = $\frac{3}{2} + \frac{1}{2}$d
octave = 2 + 1d etc.

This is the so-called mouth correction of organ pipes.[18] The length found on the monochord string is in fact not identical to the pipe length. It requires a correction, determined from pipe width, with the consequence that the wider the pipe in relation to length, the shorter the pipe body is. Since all the treatises assume the same pipe width throughout the series, the pipes become very wide at the top in relation to their length; in the medieval organ the pipes must have been severely shortened relative to their theoretical length.

However, since the treatises under examination here take the smallest pipe as standard, the picture is reversed, so that the mouth correction, relative to the smallest pipe, results in a lengthening of the larger pipes. The third group of scale treatises, including nos. 21-27, calculates pipe length by the same principles as the group above, with the sole difference that the largest pipe is used as standard, i.e. the mouth correction appears as a subtractive value.

The fourth, smallest group of scale treatises includes sources 28 and 29. In earlier treatises, e.g. 12-14, the length of the (smallest pipe) standard pipe was given as 8 .d. 28 and 29 calculate pipe length for all notes from this basis. I give below the table for 28, limited to 1 octave, adding the length scales on the basis 8 · d = 1:

---

in 10. 10 and 11 give a second possibility for calculating the semitone, claimed by them as the better one, i.e. "per diatessaron", from the fourth (= 2 whole tones + semitone) the major third (= 2 whole tones) is deducted: $\frac{3}{4} \cdot \frac{81}{64} = \frac{243}{256}$.

[18] Cf. the appropriate publications of H. Helmholtz (Crelles Journal für Mathematik, vol. 57, p.1, 1860, reprinted in : Ostwalds Klassikern der exakten Wissenschaften, vol. 80, Leipzig 1891) and Lord Rayleigh, Theory of Sound, vol. II 307, p.180 and appendix A. Phil, Trans. Roy. Loc. London, vol. 161, p.77, 1871. The explanations of Hans Hickmann (Das Portativ, Kassel, 1936, p. 136f), who takes one of the many scaling prescriptions mentioned above as "the unique document of its kind" from Buhle's papers and used it as "by far the most convincing proof of its kind" for his theory of the "distributed incomplete practical scale" are quite wrong. One can only be amazed at his complaint "unfortunately neither organ-building practice or theory can give a satisfactory answer to this problem" (i.e., what effect the addition of the diameter portion has in practice), since Riemann (Präl. u. Studien II, p. 199) and Buhle (op. cit. p.93) had already pointed in the right direction, i.e. to mouth correction. See also below, p. 22.

pipe	length given in source	length on basis of 1
I	16 d	2
II	$14\frac{2}{9}$ d	$\frac{16}{9}$
III	$13\frac{1}{2}$ d	$\frac{27}{16}$
IV	12 d	$\frac{3}{2}$
V	$10\frac{2}{3}$ d	$\frac{4}{3}$
VI	$10\frac{1}{8}$ d	$\frac{81}{64}$
VII	9 d	$\frac{9}{8}$
VIII	8 d	1

29 gives similar values, but with mouth correction also taken into account:

	length given in source	reduced to basic value and mouth correction on basis 8.d = 1
fundamental	$36\frac{1}{8}$ d	$4 + 4\frac{1}{8}$ d
fourth	$26\frac{9}{16}$ d	$3 + 2\frac{9}{16}$ d
octave	17 d	2 + 1 d
2nd fourth	$12\frac{1}{2}$ d	$\frac{3}{2} + \frac{1}{2}$ d
2nd fifth	11 d	$\frac{4}{3} + \frac{1}{3}$ d
2nd octave	8 d	1

3

It must be remembered that these scale treatises do not provide complete chromatic scales. They assume keyboards using diatonic scales[19] which often vary a great deal, as a quick glance over the sources will show. As the question of keyboard design in old organs has been considered several times already,[20] the problems of pipe length scales – raised here in passing – will be examined and the result of collating the treatises presented in table form. Only the scale prescriptions offering true series will be given, i.e. not 7 and 9-14. Mouth correction is left out

---

[19] Diatonic is used here in the sense of a series of notes consisting of a mixture of natural whole tones and semitones.

[20] Buhle's theory (op.cit. p.94), that the medieval organ first had a major scale is untenable. More recently Hans Hickmann has written about this problem. I will not go into Hickmann's conclusions in more detail. His interpretation of the sources (see above, p. 12 note 18) and conclusions drawn from measurements taken from old pictures prove that he did not take mouth correction into account, but is an attempt not to be underestimated.

here, since the first concern is to demonstrate theoretical pipe length; it will be dealt with in particular later on. The tables are arranged so as to begin with the largest pipe, as in modern practice. Where the sources take the smallest pipe as standard the tables are completed "from below". Thus the last scales in table I are calculated from the first in table II, working from the largest pipe. Calculations made by me on the basis of the text are marked as such. For reasons of space details in the tables are limited to one octave, even where the sources give scales for two. This could be done without harm, since the second octaves nearly always give halved – or doubled – values.[21] The calculation starts from the basis: 1 = largest pipe. For reasons given in detail below, the additional note letters are added, where they are supplied. The Roman numerals refer to the intervals given in the first vertical column. The second vertical column gives the pitch of each interval (in cents)[21a]; here it should be pointed out that Pythagorean scales are involved in all cases.

---

[21] Deviations are given below.

[21a] The cent is a logarithmic measurement for musical intervals. It exploits the mathematical rule that multiplication or dividing figures is the same as adding or dividing their logarithms, and thus gives each interval the logarithm of the vibration ratio concerned. For convenience logarithms on the basis of 10 are not chosen (e.g. log 2 = 0.30103); instead the basis is selected so that the logarithm of 2 (the octave's vibration ratio) receives the value 1200. For any interval with a vibration ratio of $\frac{p}{q}$ the cents value is calculated by

$$\frac{1200}{\log 2} \cdot \log\left(\frac{p}{q}\right) = 3986.3 \cdot \log\left(\frac{p}{q}\right) \text{ cents}$$

The octave has 1200 cents, the tempered semitone 100, the tempered fifth 700, the pure fifth 702, etc.

[22] Absent in the original.

[23] Apparently added to the MS later.

[24] The size of the interval between individual notes is shown by T for tonus, whole tone, or S, semitonium, semitone.

[25] The lower of the 2 octaves has the series F,G paramese, A, etc; only the higher octave gives the G trite synemmenon semitone insertion (see note 40).

[26] The lower of the two octaves has the series F,G,A etc, the higher F, synemmenon, G, A etc.

[27] Addition: "In hac ipsa incipit integer minor ordo priorque."

[28] Addition: "In hac ipsa etiam incipit integer minor ordo et prior." In 17 the text is: "Prima e (calculated from the smallest pipe) item in tres dividatur, additaque tertia cum tertia diametri habebis diatessaron in ipsa quarta peractum," but in 18

TABLE I

Interval	Related pitch in cents	Source 1	2[24]	3[25]	4[24]	15	16	17	18	20	28
I	0	[22] [1]	E 1	F 1	F 1	F 1	1	1	1	1	F 1
II	90	$9/8 \cdot \mathrm{IV}$ $= 243/256$	F $9/8 \cdot \mathrm{IV}$ or $3/2 \cdot \mathrm{IX}$ $= 243/256$	G trite synemmenon $3/2 \cdot \mathrm{IX}$ $= 243/256$	Synemmenon[26] $243/256$	—	—	$3/2 \cdot \mathrm{IX}$ $= 243/256$	$3/2 \cdot \mathrm{IX}$ $= 243/256$	$3/2 \cdot \mathrm{IX}$ $= 243/256$	—
III	204	—	or $4/3 \cdot \mathrm{VIII}$ $= 8/9$	G paramese $4/3 \cdot \mathrm{VIII}$ $= 8/9$	G $8/9$	G $8/9$	—	—	—	—	G $8/9$
IV	294	$9/8 \cdot \mathrm{VI}$ $= 27/32$	G $9/8 \cdot \mathrm{VI}$ or $4/3 \cdot \mathrm{IX}$ or $3/2 \cdot \mathrm{XI}$ $= 27/32$	A $9/8 \cdot \mathrm{VI}$ or $4/3 \cdot \mathrm{IX}$ or $3/2 \cdot \mathrm{XI}$ $= 27/32$	A $27/32$	A $27/32$	$9/8 \cdot \mathrm{VI}$ $= 27/32$	$3/2 \cdot \mathrm{XI}$ $= 27/32$	$3/2 \cdot \mathrm{XI}$ $= 27/32$	$3/2 \cdot \mathrm{XI}$ $= 27/32$	A $27/32$
V	—	—	—	—	—	—	—	—	—	—	—
VI	498	$4/3 \cdot \mathrm{XI}$ $= 3/4$	A $3/2 \cdot \mathrm{XIII}$ or $4/3 \cdot \mathrm{XI}$ or $9/8 \cdot \mathrm{VIII}$ $= 3/4$	B $9/8 \cdot \mathrm{VIII}$ or $4/3 \cdot \mathrm{XI}$ or $3/2 \cdot \mathrm{XIII}$ $= 3/4$	B $3/4$	B $3/4$	$3/2 \cdot \mathrm{XIII}$ or $9/8 \cdot \mathrm{VIII}$ $= 3/4$	$3/2 \cdot \mathrm{XIII}$ $= 3/4$	$3/2 \cdot \mathrm{XIII}$ $= 3/4$	$3/2 \cdot \mathrm{XIII}$ $= 3/4$	B $3/4$
VII	588	$9/8 \cdot \mathrm{IX}$ $= 729/1024$	—	—	—	—	—	Synemmenon $9/8 \cdot \mathrm{IX}$ $= 729/1024$	[28] [$9/8 \cdot \mathrm{IX}$ $= 729/1024$]	Synemmenon $3/4 \cdot \mathrm{II}$ $= 729/1024$	—
VIII	702	—	B $4/3 \cdot \mathrm{XIII}$ $= 2/3$	C $4/3 \cdot \mathrm{XIII}$ $= 2/3$	C $2/3$	C $2/3$	$4/3 \cdot \mathrm{XIII}$ $= 2/3$	$4/3 \cdot \mathrm{XIII}$[27] $= 2/3$	—	$4/3 \cdot \mathrm{XIII}$ $= 2/3$	C $2/3$
IX	792	$9/8 \cdot \mathrm{XI}$ $= 81/128$	C $9/8 \cdot \mathrm{XI}$ $= 81/128$	D $9/8 \cdot \mathrm{XI}$ $= 81/128$	D $81/128$	D $81/128$	$9/8 \cdot \mathrm{XI}$ $= 81/128$	$9/8 \cdot \mathrm{XI}$ $= 81/128$	$9/8 \cdot \mathrm{XI}$ $= 81/128$	$3/4 \cdot \mathrm{IV}$ $= 81/128$	D $81/128$
X	904	—	—	—	—	—	—	—	[Synemmenon[29] $5/6 \cdot \mathrm{VII}$ $= 3645/6144$]	—	—
XI	996	$9/8 \cdot \mathrm{XIII}$ $= 9/16$	D $9/8 \cdot \mathrm{XIII}$ $= 9/16$	E $9/8 \cdot \mathrm{XIII}$ $= 9/16$	E $9/16$	E $9/16$	$9/8 \cdot \mathrm{XIII}$ $= 9/16$	$9/8 \cdot \mathrm{XIII}$ $= 9/16$	$9/8 \cdot \mathrm{XIII}$ $= 9/16$	$3/4 \cdot \mathrm{VI}$ $= 9/16$	E $9/16$
XII	1086	$3/4 \cdot \mathrm{VII}$[23] $= 2187/4096$	—	—	—	—	—	—	—	—	—
XIII	1200	$1/2$	E $1/2$	F $1/2$	F $1/2$	F $1/2$	$1/2$	$1/2$	$1/2$	$1/2$	F $1/2$

Table II offers a unified picture; all the series give the major scale, except that the septime is present in 6 and 21 (earlier text), 27 (earlier text) and 24 as minor seventh, and some sources (8, 21 – later text – 22, 23, 25, 26 and 27 – later text) offer major and minor seventh together. 5, 6 and 8 also give C as fundamental (= A in the Old French

---

"Tertia item in octo dividatur, additaque octava cum tertia (!) diametri, habebis diatessaron, quod praediximus integrum in ipsa quarta peractum." It can clearly be seen that 17 has the earlier text, which is only imperfectly different from 18 in that the mouth correction is given as $\frac{1}{3}$d, as in 17, instead of $\frac{1}{8}$d, which would have been correct. The whole tone reached from the third is not the "integrum diatessaron", rather the extended quint (see also note 29).

[29] The original text is: "Tertia (calculated from the smallest pipe) item fistula in sex dividatur addita tamen octava diametri, et sic sexta in summitate reiecta, in quinto synemmenon invenitur." Riemann's view, that it would be better to read "secunda" for "tertia" (Studien zur Geschichte der Notenschrift, p. 308), overlooks the fact that the pipe series is built up from the smallest pipe, so that the value of $\frac{5}{6}$ × the second smallest pipe is already less than the value of the smallest pipe. I read "quarta" for "tertia", which agrees with the scale sequence, also in the second octave: third, fourth, synemmenon, fifth. It is not possible to be fully clear about this. It seems as if the keyboard arrangement offered in 17 is altered in 18, but the text provided by 17 largely retains the original conception and arrangement. Hickmann (see op.cit. p.136) interprets the passage as if the value of the synemmenon were $\frac{7}{6}$ × third; then the "in quinto" would have to be suppressed. In other points Hickmann's reading can hardly be upheld.

[30] The text reads: "Sed sic temperatur quarta, ut ter ducta cum tertia parte implet primam." If "fistula" is read for "ter ducta", the fourth = $\frac{3}{4}$, since $\frac{3}{4} + \frac{1}{3} . \frac{3}{4} = 1$.

[31] The tenth is given as C, thus the fundamental is A. The passage runs: "Deficientibus itaque minoribus fistulis sicut in praesenti loco decimo faciunt, qui C litteram notantur." Buhle (see op. cit., p. 96, note 2) alters the text quite unreasonably to "sicut in praesenti loco decimo quinto faciunt."

[32] Source M (see Paul Piper, op. cit. 851f) does not yet mention the synemmenon, but gives the minor seventh only. Later sources give the minor seventh as synemmenon and add the major seventh.

[33] 27 gives the values for seventh and octave twice. This is probably due to the details about the synemmenon being added from another source, and thus written out again. The section: "Hic inseritur synemmenon . . ." to " haec est longitudo eius " is the later insertion. The value given in tract 27 for the seventh beside that in the text ($\frac{9}{8}$ of the sixth is $\frac{3}{4}$ the fourth = synemmenon. Hence 27 originally had the same construction as 24 or 21 in the original version. The second value given for the octave $\frac{8}{9}$ the seventh (in the text the sixth is given) only agrees if the seventh is taken as a minor seventh ($\frac{9}{16}$).

[34] Gives $\frac{2}{3}$ of the third as the octave value ($\frac{64}{81} . \frac{2}{3} = \frac{128}{243}$ = seventh); probably $\frac{2}{3}$ of the fourth ($\frac{3}{4} . \frac{2}{3} = \frac{1}{2}$= octave) is intended.

[35] In 25 $\frac{8}{8}$ is given in error instead of $\frac{8}{9}$.

TABLE II

Interval	Related pitch in cents		Source						
	for source *5*	for remaining sources	*5*	*6*	*8*	*21,27*	*22,23*	*24*	*25,26*
I	0	0	A 1	[A] [31] 1	A 1	1	1	1	1
II	—	—	—	—	—	—	—	—	—
III	231	204	B $^{7}/_{8} \cdot \mathrm{I}$ $= {}^{7}/_{8}$	[B] $^{8}/_{9} \cdot \mathrm{I}$ $= {}^{8}/_{9}$	B $^{4}/_{3} \cdot \mathrm{VIII}$ $= {}^{8}/_{9}$	$^{8}/_{9} \cdot \mathrm{I}$ $= {}^{8}/_{9}$	$^{8}/_{9} \cdot \mathrm{I}$ $= {}^{8}/_{9}$	$^{8}/_{9} \cdot \mathrm{I}$ $= {}^{8}/_{9}$	$^{8}/_{9} \cdot \mathrm{I}$ [35] $= {}^{8}/_{9}$
IV	—	—	—	—	—	—	—	—	—
V	462	408	C $^{7}/_{8} \cdot \mathrm{III}$ $= {}^{49}/_{64}$	[C] $^{8}/_{9} \cdot \mathrm{III}$ $= {}^{64}/_{81}$	C $^{4}/_{3} \cdot \mathrm{X}$ $= {}^{64}/_{81}$	$^{8}/_{9} \cdot \mathrm{III}$ $= {}^{64}/_{81}$	$^{8}/_{9} \cdot \mathrm{III}$ $= {}^{64}/_{81}$	$^{8}/_{9} \cdot \mathrm{III}$ $= {}^{64}/_{81}$	$^{8}/_{9} \cdot \mathrm{III}$ $= {}^{64}/_{81}$
VI	498	498	D [30] $^{3}/_{4} \cdot \mathrm{I}$ $= {}^{3}/_{4}$	[D] $^{3}/_{4} \cdot \mathrm{I}$ $= {}^{3}/_{4}$	D $^{3}/_{4} \cdot \mathrm{I}$ $= {}^{3}/_{4}$	$^{3}/_{4} \cdot \mathrm{I}$ $= {}^{3}/_{4}$	$^{3}/_{4} \cdot \mathrm{I}$ $= {}^{3}/_{4}$	$^{3}/_{4} \cdot \mathrm{I}$ $= {}^{3}/_{4}$	$^{3}/_{4} \cdot \mathrm{I}$ $= {}^{3}/_{4}$
VII	—	—	—	—	—	—	—	—	—
VIII	729	702	E $^{7}/_{8} \cdot \mathrm{VI}$ $= {}^{21}/_{32}$	[E] $^{8}/_{9} \cdot \mathrm{VI}$ $= {}^{2}/_{3}$	E $= {}^{2}/_{3} \cdot \mathrm{I}$ $= {}^{2}/_{3}$	$^{2}/_{3} \cdot \mathrm{I}$ $= {}^{2}/_{3}$	$^{2}/_{3} \cdot \mathrm{I}$ $= {}^{2}/_{3}$	$^{3}/_{4} \cdot \mathrm{III}$ $= {}^{2}/_{3}$	$^{2}/_{3} \cdot \mathrm{I}$ $= {}^{2}/_{3}$
IX	—	—	—	—	—	—	—	—	—
X	960	906	F $^{7}/_{8} \cdot \mathrm{VIII}$ $= {}^{147}/_{256}$	[F] $^{8}/_{9} \cdot \mathrm{VIII}$ $= {}^{16}/_{27}$	F $^{2}/_{3} \cdot \mathrm{III}$ $= {}^{16}/_{27}$	$^{8}/_{9} \cdot \mathrm{VIII}$ $= {}^{16}/_{27}$	$^{8}/_{9} \cdot \mathrm{VIII}$ $= {}^{16}/_{27}$	$^{3}/_{4} \cdot \mathrm{V}$ $= {}^{16}/_{27}$	$^{2}/_{3} \cdot \mathrm{III}$ $= {}^{16}/_{27}$
XI	—	996	—	[G] $^{3}/_{4} \cdot \mathrm{VI}$ $= {}^{9}/_{16}$	Synemmenon $^{3}/_{4} \cdot \mathrm{VI}$ $= {}^{9}/_{16}$	earlier text: Septime $= {}^{3}/_{4} \cdot \mathrm{VI}$ later text: Synemmenon $= {}^{3}/_{4} \cdot \mathrm{VI}$ $= {}^{9}/_{16}$ [32] [33]	Synemmenon $^{3}/_{4} \cdot \mathrm{VI}$ $= {}^{9}/_{16}$	$^{3}/_{4} \cdot \mathrm{VI}$ $= {}^{9}/_{16}$	Synemmenon $^{3}/_{4} \cdot \mathrm{VI}$ $= {}^{9}/_{16}$
XII	1191	1110	G $^{7}/_{8} \cdot \mathrm{X}$ $= {}^{1029}/_{2048}$	—	G $^{2}/_{3} \cdot \mathrm{V}$ $= {}^{128}/_{243}$	earlier text: — later text: Septime $= {}^{8}/_{9} \cdot \mathrm{X}$ $= {}^{128}/_{243}$ [32] [33]	$^{8}/_{9} \cdot \mathrm{X}$ $= {}^{128}/_{243}$	—	$^{2}/_{3} \cdot \mathrm{V}$ $= {}^{128}/_{243}$
XIII	1200	1200	A $^{1}/_{2}$	[A] $^{8}/_{9} \cdot \mathrm{XI} = {}^{1}/_{2}$	[A] $^{1}/_{2}$	$^{1}/_{2} \cdot \mathrm{I}$ [33] or $^{8}/_{9} \cdot \mathrm{XI}$ $= {}^{1}/_{2}$	$^{1}/_{2}$	$^{2}/_{3} \cdot \mathrm{VI}$ [34] $= {}^{1}/_{2}$	$^{1}/_{2}$

system).[36] Elsewhere G as fundamental and the scale G, A, B, c, d, e, f and g are supposed, where only the minor seventh occurs. It must also be observed that both b flat and f sharp can be indicated with the synemmenon. For 21 and 22 G must certainly be accepted as fundamental.[37]

Table I has quite a different appearance, showing clearly that the major scale is not involved here, nor any common scale. 2 gives E as fundamental. Here Odo's designation can be supposed and the series E, F or F sharp G, A, B, C, D, E.[38] obtained. With 3 and 4 the old French system is concerned; both provide scales of A, B flat (or B),[39] C, D, E, F, G and A. In 1 the scale is probably B, C, D, E, F, G, A, B, except that here a B flat has been inserted (probably by a later author) between A and B, the synemmenon.[40] 15 and 28, which have F in the Old French system as their fundamental, i.e. our A, have the following key sequence: A, B, C, D, E, F, G, A. 16 seems to concur with this except for the missing B, beginning thus A, C, D, etc. 17 explicitly gives the transition to the "small ordo" between VIII and IX, i.e. the lesser octave, B-c, hence the sequence is to be shown as: E, F, G, A, B flat (the synemmenon), B, c, d, e . . . Whether 18 is the same as 17 is an open question, given the difficulty of source identification. If the version I give in table I is correct, we obtain the series A, B flat, C, D, E flat, F sharp (synemmenon), G, A. 20 can easily be analysed as identical to 17 by the appearance of the synemmenon. Table III provides a survey of the scales yielded from tables I and II.

Table III is interesting from many points of view. It sheds definite light on the organ keyboards of the middle ages and also confirms in a surprising way the thesis that the minor scale is an inversion of the

---

[36] Old French: A B flat C D E F etc; modern: c d e f g etc.

[37] Because the length of the lowest pipe in both tracts is given as $1\frac{1}{2}$ ells or 3′, roughly equalling our C $2\frac{2}{3}$′ (not C 4′, as Buhle, op. cit. above, p.94, and O. Walcker, following him, on the Freiburg Organ Congress, Augsburg, 1926, p. 43). This agrees with the Berne *anon*, that the form on which the pipes are to be beaten round, and which should always be a little longer than the largest pipe, should be "almost 4 ft long".

[38] I only give an octave in every case, as the continuation is understood.

[39] In the higher octave B flat and B, the lower, only B.

[40] A term taken from Greek musical theory, used in the medieval tracts for the note B flat.

[41] Only in the higher octave.

[42] The second column gives possibilities for 21, later text, 22, 23, 25, 26, 27, later version.

TABLE III

Keyboard	*1*	*2*	*3*	*4*	*15*	*16*	*17*	*18*	*20*	*28*	*21* earlier text *24* *27* earlier text	*5*	*6*	*8,21* later text *22,23,25,26,27* later text [42]	
C												C	C	C	or
D												D	D	D	
E		E					E		E			E	E	E	
F		F					F		F			F	F	F	
F♯		or F♯													
G		G					G		G		G	G	G	G	G
A		A	A	A	A	A	A	A	A	A	A	A	A	A	A
B♭		—	B♭[41]	B♭[41]	—	—	B♭	B♭	B♭	—	—	—	B♭	B♭	—
B	B	B	B	B	B	—	B	—	B	B	B	B	—	B	B
c	c	c	c	c	c	c	c	c	c	c	c	c	c	c	c
d	d	d	d	d	d	d	d	d	d	d	d				d
e	e	e	e	e	e	e	e	e♯	e	e	e				e
f	f		f	f	f	f		f		f	f				f
f♯								f♯							f♯
g	g		g	g	g	g		g		g	g				g
a	a		a	a	a	a		a		a					
b♭	b♭														
b	b														
c′															

major. Tracts 5, 6, 8 and 11-27, with scales derived from the largest pipe, i.e. from bass to treble, all show the major scale, as table III indicates, or a related scale. Sources 2-4 15-18, 20 and 28 achieve the construction of the scale from the smallest pipe; the scales of these treatises start at A or E and are very closely related to the modern minor. Thus it can be seen that the sentence above, which should actually be expressed, considering the chronological sequence of the treatises, as the major scale as the inversion of the minor, was not only consciously felt in the middle ages, it was also the basis of calculation in practice.

4

As already mentioned, mouth correction is determined in the majority of sources from parts of the diameter, constant for the whole series. For simplicity I give the calculated results here in tabular form (table IV). The following is to be observed; it has already been indicated above that, of the sources in question here, tracts 9-20 and 29 take the smallest pipe as standard and the mouth correction thus appears over the course of the series (going towards the largest pipe) as a continually increasing addition value, which is 0 for the smallest pipe, and normally 3·d for the largest pipe two octaves above. Tracts 21-27 take the largest pipe as point of departure; thus mouth correction appears as a constantly increasing subtraction value going towards the smallest pipes. So as to bring the results of both methods together for comparision in one table, the length of the largest pipe in the treatises 21-27 is taken as 1+3·d. The given figures are calculated as multiples or parts of the diameter .[43] The first vertical column gives the semitone intervals for 2 octaves in Roman numerals.

---

[43] As is now the practice of determining mouth correction from pipe diameter.

[44] For 9 the text given in Gerbert II, 277 runs: 'Si fistula . . . insuper diametri inter mensuram contineat.' Gerbert corrects "in se." But the right text has "ter" (also the Paris MS and the Berne codex). This figure is not given at all in 12, 13 and 14. In 11 the value of mouth correction for the longest pipe is given as 4·d.

[45] Absent in 11. In 10 erroneously 1 instead of $\frac{1}{3}$ (. . . nec non et [tertiam] diametri . . .).

[46] Absent in 9 and 10. In 12 the text is: major habeat minorem totum diametrum (recte: totam et diametrum).

[47] Absent in 9, 12, 13 and 14. In 10 and 11 $\frac{64}{243}$·d is given as a further value for the semitone mouth correction.

[48] Instead of "cum tertia diametri", "cum octava diametri." See 28.

TABLE IV

	9-14	15	16	17	18	19	20	21&27	22&25	23	24	26	29
I	3 [44]	$4\frac{1}{8}$		3	3	3	3	3	3	3	3	3	$4\frac{1}{8}$
II		$3\frac{31}{72}$		$2\frac{51}{64}$	$2\frac{51}{64}$		$2\frac{17}{64}$						
III								$2\frac{5}{9}$	$2\frac{5}{9}$ [53]	$2\frac{5}{9}$	$2\frac{5}{9}$	$2\frac{5}{9}$	
IV		$3\frac{19}{128}$		$2\frac{3}{8}$	$2\frac{3}{8}$		$2\frac{1}{8}$						
V								$2\frac{4}{81}$	$2\frac{13}{81}$	$2\frac{4}{81}$	$2\frac{13}{81}$	$2\frac{4}{81}$ [56] or $2\frac{13}{81}$	
VI		$2\frac{9}{16}$		2	2	2	2	2	2	2 [54]	2	2	$2\frac{9}{16}$
VII				$1\frac{217}{256}$	$[1\frac{217}{256}]$ [48]		$1\frac{217}{768}$						
VIII		$2\frac{1}{24}$		$1\frac{2}{3}$			$1\frac{2}{3}$	$1\frac{2}{3}$	$1\frac{2}{3}$	$1\frac{2}{3}$	$1\frac{2}{3}$	$1\frac{2}{3}$	
IX		$1\frac{425}{512}$		$1\frac{17}{32}$	$1\frac{17}{32}$		$1\frac{17}{96}$						
X					$[1\frac{1405}{1536}]$ [49]			$1\frac{10}{27}$	$1\frac{10}{27}$	$1\frac{10}{27}$	$1\frac{10}{27}$	$1\frac{10}{27}$	
XI		$1\frac{25}{64}$		$1\frac{1}{4}$	$1\frac{1}{4}$		$1\frac{1}{12}$	earlier text: $1\frac{1}{4}$ later text: $1\frac{1}{8}$	$1\frac{1}{4}$	$1\frac{1}{8}$	$1\frac{1}{4}$	$1\frac{1}{8}$ [56] or $1\frac{1}{4}$	
XII								later text: $1\frac{26}{243}$	$1\frac{26}{243}$	$1\frac{26}{243}$		$1\frac{8}{243}$ or [56] $1\frac{26}{243}$	
XIII	1	1	0	1	1	$1\frac{1}{8}$	1	1	1	1	1 [55]	1	1
XIV				$\frac{115}{128}$	$\frac{115}{128}$		$\frac{81}{128}$						
XV		$\frac{7}{9}$						$\frac{7}{9}$	$\frac{7}{9}$	$\frac{7}{9}$	$\frac{7}{9}$		
XVI		$\frac{11}{16}$	$\frac{11}{16}$	$\frac{11}{16}$	$\frac{11}{16}$		$\frac{9}{16}$						
XVII								$\frac{85}{162}$	$\frac{47}{81}$	$\frac{85}{162}$	$\frac{47}{81}$	$\frac{85}{162}$ or [56] $\frac{47}{81}$	
XVIII	$\frac{1}{2}$	$\frac{1}{2}$	$\frac{1}{2}$	$\frac{1}{2}$	$\frac{1}{2}$	$\frac{9}{16}$ [50] or $\frac{5}{8}$	$\frac{1}{2}$	$\frac{1}{2}$	$\frac{1}{2}$	$\frac{1}{2}$	$\frac{1}{2}$	$\frac{1}{2}$	$\frac{1}{2}$
XIX				$\frac{217}{512}$	$[\frac{217}{512}]$ [48]		$\frac{217}{1536}$						
XX	$\frac{1}{3}$ [45]	$\frac{1}{3}$	$\frac{1}{3}$	$\frac{1}{3}$		$\frac{28}{99}$ [51] or $\frac{4}{11}$	$\frac{1}{3}$	$\frac{1}{3}$	$\frac{1}{3}$	$\frac{1}{3}$	$\frac{1}{3}$	$\frac{1}{3}$	$\frac{1}{3}$
XXI		$\frac{17}{64}$	$\frac{17}{64}$	$\frac{17}{64}$	$\frac{17}{64}$		$\frac{17}{192}$						
XXII					$[\frac{1405}{3072}]$ [49]			$\frac{5}{27}$	$\frac{5}{27}$	$\frac{5}{27}$	$\frac{5}{27}$	$\frac{5}{27}$	
XXIII	$\frac{1}{8}$ [46]	$\frac{1}{8}$	$\frac{1}{8}$	$\frac{1}{8}$	$\frac{1}{8}$	$\frac{1}{8}$	$\frac{1}{24}$	earlier text: $\frac{1}{8}$ later text: $\frac{1}{16}$	$\frac{1}{8}$	$\frac{1}{16}$	$\frac{1}{8}$	$\frac{1}{16}$ [56] or $\frac{1}{8}$	
XXIV	$\frac{1}{16}$ [47]							later text: $\frac{13}{243}$	$\frac{13}{243}$	$\frac{13}{243}$		$\frac{4}{243}$ [56] or $\frac{13}{243}$	
XXV	0	0	0	0	0	0	0	0 [52]	0	0	0	0	0

A check on the material in table IV is provided by the first formula for calculating the mouth correction of pipe x. Here μ equals the mouth correction in parts of the diameter as an additive value to the length, calculated theoretically from the standard pipe; l_a signifies the length of the standard pipe as the smallest pipe and l_x the theoretic length of pipe x:

$$\mu = \left(\frac{l_x}{l_a} - 1\right) \cdot d \tag{1}$$

The true pipe length is then $l_x + \mu$.[57]
This formula is valid with limited exceptions for tracts 9 (where the mouth correction for semitones and whole tones is absent), 10-14, 16-18; 20 provides more notable exceptions.

The following reworking of formula 1 can be used with the scale

---

[49] See note 29 on the textual possibilities. The result does not agree because of the "addita tamen octava diametri." Cf table II, note 32, for the details of septime and octave.

[50] The original has: "et mediatatis octavam, et octavae octavam." It is questionable whether this should read "et huius octavae octavam," so that the solution should be $\frac{1}{2.8} + \frac{1}{2.8.8} = \frac{9}{128} = \frac{9}{16}$ d, or whether $\frac{1}{2.8} + \frac{1}{8.8} = \frac{5}{64} = \frac{5}{8}$ d is intended. (8d = 1 is assumed; on this see p. 31 below).

[51] Original text: "et tertiae undecimam [the source, Gerbert I, 328a here has decimam, wrongly] et undecimae sextam." For the same reasons as in note 50 it is questionable whether $\frac{1}{3 \cdot 11} + \frac{1}{3 \cdot 11 \cdot 6} = \frac{7}{198} = \frac{28}{99}$d or $\frac{1}{3 \cdot 11} + \frac{1}{11 \cdot 6} = \frac{1}{22} = \frac{4}{11}$d is meant. (8d= 1, see note 50).

[52] The older text 27 calculates the octave from the sixth (more correctly, seventh: see note 33). Thus a value of $\frac{9}{8}$ is obtained instead of 0 for mouth correction. The faultiness of this calculation is obvious.

[53] 25 correction: see note 35

[54] 23 has the text: "in qua excipiatur nova pars diametri . . ." This should be "tertia."

[55] 24: cf table II, note 34.

[56] The second set of figures is introduced by the formula "vel potius." K.G. Fellerer, in Beiträge zur Musikgeschichte Freisings, p. 25, wishes to infer from this that 26 was completed before 25, since 25 only gives the second better values for the mouth correction. But table IV shows that other tracts (12, 23, 27) also have the figures given first in 26, which, besides, do not follow the otherwise applied calculation laws (see above) and thus could have been developed later from practical experience. The precepts 17 and 18, contained in the same tracts, also seem to me (because of the source detail present in 17) to prove Aribo's script the older.

[57] One example: $l_a = \frac{1}{2}$. $l_x = \frac{16}{27}$; $\mu = \left(\frac{\frac{6}{27}}{\frac{1}{2}} - 1\right) d = \frac{5}{27}$d

precepts 21-27, where the standard pipe is the largest, and mouth correction thus appears as a subtraction value;

$$\mu = \left(1 - \frac{l_x}{l_a}\right) d \tag{2}$$

In this case the true pipe length amounts to $l_x - \mu$.

Tract 19 determines mouth correction by parts of the length of the standard pipe, not of the diameter. However, as it gives the length of the standard pipe as 8×diameter, like sources 12 and 13, e.g., a conversion into diameter parts is easily possible, proving that 19 is also conformed to the first formula developed above.

15 is a special case. This source, (as does 4, deriving from the same author) calculates pipe lengths by adding so-called "differences", not multiplication of the standard pipe value with an appropriate ratio. Thus the following theoretic pipe lengths can be obtained where the pipe length A = 192:

key	theoretic pipe length	difference	where 192=1
A	192		1
		24	
G	216		$\frac{9}{8}$
		27	
F	243		$\frac{81}{64}$
		13	
E	256		$\frac{4}{3}$
		32	
D	288		$\frac{3}{2}$
	etc.		

The "differences" make it possible to calculate pipe lengths conveniently using other basic values. Thus if the octave starting with A-2304 is taken, i.e. 12× the initial member of the series just mentioned, the difference figures set out above need only be multiplied by 12 to obtain the difference figures of the new series;

key	difference	theoretic pipe length	theoretic pipe length where 2304=1
A		= 2304	1
G	12×24 = 288	288+2304 = 2592	$\frac{9}{8}$
F	12×27 = 324	324+2592 = 2916	$\frac{81}{64}$
E	12×13 = 156	156+2916 = 3072	$\frac{4}{3}$
D	12×32 = 384	384+3072 = 3456	$\frac{3}{2}$
		etc	

Source 15 finds mouth correction and thus, true pipe length, in this way; the difference figures are multiplied by $13\frac{1}{2}$ (in the higher octave) and $14\frac{11}{32}$ (in the lower), not the natural factor 12. The result, agreeing with formula 1, is:

key	difference	true pipe length	where 2304 = 1	separated into basic value and mouth correction[58]
A		= 2304	1	1
G	$13\frac{1}{2} \times 24 = 324$	$324 + 2304 = 2628$	$\frac{73}{61}$	$\frac{9}{8} + \frac{1}{8}$ d
F	$13\frac{1}{2} \times 27 = 364\frac{1}{2}$	$364\frac{1}{2} + 2628 = 2992\frac{1}{2}$	$\frac{665}{512}$	$\frac{81}{64} + \frac{17}{64}$ d
E	$13\frac{1}{2} \times 13 = 175\frac{1}{2}$	$175\frac{1}{2} + 2992\frac{1}{2} = 3168$	$\frac{11}{8}$	$\frac{4}{3} + \frac{1}{3}$ d
D	$13\frac{1}{2} \times 32 = 432$	$432 + 3168 = 3600$	$\frac{25}{16}$	$\frac{3}{2} + \frac{1}{2}$ d

The results of individual calculations brought together in table IV show that formula 1 is true also for 15 in the upper octave, and for the lower, this formula is to be used.

$$\mu = \frac{25\frac{l_x}{l_a} - 34}{16} \qquad (3)$$

The values of 29[59] and an arrangement calculated by Gerbert himself as a comment on 19 (Gerbert I,328a) agree with the calculations of this formula.

Formulae 1-3 and the old scale precepts are based on a standard pipe of length l_a, from which the theoretical length 1_a of the remaining pipes is calculated. The true length L is produced from l_x by addition (formulae 1 and 3; the standard pipe is the smallest pipe in the series), or subtraction (formula 2; standard pipe = largest pipe in the series) of mouth correction μ. Thus $L = l_x + \mu$. With the standard pipe theoretic and real length coincide; μ is thus 0 and $1_a = L_a$.

Today it is normal in calculating theoretical pipe length to start from the length, the air column vibrating in the pipe, not a pre-given standard pipe. From this mouth correction is to be subtracted to obtain the real

---

[58] Here mouth correction is given as parts of the diameter [8.d = length of standard pipe = 1].

[59] Hence it can be concluded that this formula is a distinctive feature of Bernelinus; of course his "Mensura fistularum et monochordi" also has other values (cf 19).

pipe length. Thus it becomes clear that the length of the ancients' standard pipe as a calculation basis for the theoretical length then today represents a "real" pipe length, in which mouth correction is already accounted for: $\lambda_a - \alpha = l_a = L_a$. According to the results of various researchers (cf Handbuch der Physik, vol 8, pp 254,ff) mouth correction as it is understood today, within certain limits, however, is independent of pipe length and is given as fractions of pipe diameter.

It may now be asked how the ancients' mouth correction μ can be arrived at when the modern theoretic pipe length λ_a is taken as basis, not the standard pipe l_a. The surprising result, whose development can only be outlined in passing here, [59a] is that mouth correction then becomes a constant, equal to d with the tracts using formulae 1 and 2. The following table, setting the medieval and modern methods of determining real pipe length side by side will best make clear what is involved here.

Table V shows that the practical results of both methods of calculation are the same, and that the real lengths calculated from the theoretical (as it seems today) pre-suppose a constant mouth correction of the size of the pipe diameter. Only in the few tracts proceeding according to formula 3 is a mouth correction to the advantage of the large pipes chosen in the lower octave.

59a

Given:

$$\lambda_a = L_a + \alpha \quad ; \quad \lambda_x = L_x + \alpha \quad ;$$

$$l_a = L_a \quad ; \quad l_x = L_x + \mu_x \, ;$$

$$\lambda_a : \lambda_x = l_a : l_x$$

Hence:

$$\lambda_a : \lambda_x = L_a : (L_x + \mu_x)$$

$$= (\lambda_a - \alpha) : (\lambda_x + \mu_x - \alpha)$$

$$\mu_x = \frac{\alpha \cdot (\lambda_a - \lambda_x)}{\lambda_a} = \alpha \cdot \left(1 - \frac{\lambda_x}{\lambda_a}\right)$$

In formula (2) $\mu_x = d \cdot \left(1 - \frac{l_x}{l_a}\right)$, i.e.

$$\alpha \cdot \left(1 - \frac{\lambda_x}{\lambda_a}\right) = d \cdot \left(1 - \frac{l_x}{l_a}\right).$$

But since according to the data, $\frac{\lambda_x}{\lambda_a} = \frac{l_x}{l_a}$ it follows that $\alpha = d$.

This conclusion is of some importance. A. Cavaillé-Coll, one of the first to concern himself with the problem of mouth correction (cf session report of the Paris Académie des Sciences I, 50, no 4, Paris 1860), gives mouth correction as double the pipe depth (measured in the middle of the labium). Since medieval pipes had very wide mouths and the labium took up half the pipe circumference, according to the details in the comprehensive tracts, thus pipe depth = $\frac{d}{2}$, using Cavaillé-Coll's formula, d being the doubled pipe depth. But this is the mouth correction at the base of the medieval pipe calculations. The medieval masters thus calculated mouth correction following rules publicized around the middle of the last century as apparently quite new discoveries'. J. Schmidt-Görg (Kirchenmusik. Jahrbuch 1932, p. 64) rightly states: "A problem which yet another of the most famous recent organ-builders thought he was the first to consider and solve was grasped and dealt with almost a thousand years before him in practice."

In modern physics mouth correction is given as $0.3 \cdot d$ to $0.4 \cdot d$ (cf Handbuch der Physik, op. cit.). Here it must be remembered that closed tubes, often also provided with mouth flanges, are used in the experiments. The fact that the experience of nearly a thousand years in organ-building produces a value for mouth correction $2\frac{1}{2}$ to 3 times as great as that supplied by physical observation and measurement, may be explained by the additional and complicated procedures carried out at the pipe mouth. The basic conclusion that mouth correction is only dependent on pipe diameter is nevertheless, seen from an historical point of view, a considerable one.

5

On the question of dating the groups of treatises concerned here; those in the third group (*21-27*) are certainly the latest of the sources discussed. They take the largest pipe as standard, and are influenced in their structure by the scale we call "major" today. It may be supposed that the author of the oldest source in this group (*21*), Notker Labeo (d.1022) was the same person who thought out and brought into use the method of calculating pipe length discussed here.[60]

The question whether the first (*1-8*) or the second group (*9-20*) of

---

[60] The Musica of Aribo Scholasticus designates tract *17* as "Nova fistularum mensura," *25* as "Antiqua fistularum mensura", but this description seems to be largely accounted for by the fact that *17* was made accessible directly to Aribo by abbot Wilhelm of Hirsau, probably as his own work.

TABLE V

(Diameter for all pipes is constant = d)

Pipe	Modern conversion			Medieval conversion			
	λ = theoretical pipe length (modern)	α = mouth correction (constant) = d = $\frac{1}{8}$ smallest pipe = 2	$L = \lambda - \alpha$ = real pipe length	l = theoretical pipe length (medieval). Length of standard pipe l_a = 16	μ = mouth correction (variable) by formula (1). d = $\frac{1}{8}$ smallest pipe = 2	$L = l + \mu$ = real pipe length	I.
Prime	72	2	70	$4 \cdot l_a = 64$	6	70	Formula (1)
1st. fourth	$^3/_4$ of prime = 54	2	52	$3 \cdot l_a = 48$	4	52	
1st. fifth	$^2/_3$ ” ” = 48	2	46	$^8/_3 \cdot l_a = 42^2/_3$	$3^1/_3$	46	
1st. octave	$^1/_2$ ” ” = 36	2	34	$2 \cdot l_a = 32$	2	34	
2nd. fourth	$^3/_4$ of octave = 27	2	25	$^3/_2 \cdot l_a = 24$	1	25	
2nd. fifth	$^2/_3$ ” ” = 24	2	22	$^4/_3 \cdot l_a = 21^1/_3$	$^2/_3$	22	
2nd. octave	$^1/_2$ ” ” = 18	2	16	$l_a = 16$	0	16	
	λ (see above)	α (see above)	L (see above)	l (see above) Length of standard pipe (l_a) = 70	μ by formula (2). d (see above)	$L = l - \mu$	II.
Prime	72	2	70	$l_a = 70$	0	70	Formula (2)
1st. fourth	$^3/_4$ of prime = 54	2	52	$^3/_4 \cdot l_a = 52^1/_2$	$^1/_2$	52	
1st. fifth	$^2/_3$ ” ” = 48	2	46	$^2/_3 \cdot l_a = 46^2/_3$	$^2/_3$	46	
1st. octave	$^1/_2$ ” ” = 36	2	34	$^1/_2 \cdot l_a = 35$	1	34	
2nd. fourth	$^3/_4$ of octave = 27	2	25	$^3/_8 \cdot l_a = 26^1/_4$	$^5/_4$	25	
2nd. fifth	$^2/_3$ ” ” = 24	2	22	$^1/_3 \cdot l_a = 23^1/_3$	$^4/_3$	22	
2nd. octave	$^1/_2$ ” ” = 18	2	16	$^1/_4 \cdot l_a = 17^1/_2$	$^3/_2$	16	
	λ (see above)	α gradually increases in the lower octaves until the upper octaves begin α = d = 2 becomes	L (see above)	l (see above) length of standard pipe (l_a) = 16	μ in the lower octave calculated by formula (3).d (see above)	$L = l + \mu$	III.
Prime	72	$-^1/_4$	$72^1/_4$	$4 \cdot l_a = 64$	$8^1/_4$	$72^1/_4$	Formula (3)
1st. fourth	$^3/_4$ of prime = 54	$^7/_8$	$53^1/_8$	$3 \cdot l_a = 48$	$5^1/_8$	$53^1/_8$	
1st. fifth	$^2/_3$ ” ” = 48	$1^1/_4$	$46^3/_4$	$^8/_3 \cdot l_a = 42^2/_3$	$4^1/_{12}$	$46^3/_4$	
1st. octave	$^1/_2$ ” ” = 36	2	34	$2 \cdot l_a = 32$	2	34	
	Continuation as under I			Continuation as under I			
2nd. octave	$^1/_2$ of octave = 18	2	16	$l_a = 16$	0	16	

the scale treatises is the earlier is a more difficult one. Sources *5* and *6* differ here by taking the largest pipe as standard and thus they belong to a later period. The first group could be decided upon as the earlier, since mouth correction is still not present in it. And no doubt many scale precepts in this group are very old. But the absence of mouth correction alone is not decisive; in certain circumstances (see section 6) it could indicate fairly late origin. The second group and the type of scaling represented by it is already evidenced by source *9* for the 9th century. The fourth group (*28* and *29*) can only be given a sure date in that it must be near the second group, since the smallest pipe is used as standard; the scaling method used here probably goes back to Bernelinus.

6

The scale treatises of the late middle ages, e.g. that by Georgius Anselmi,[61] cease to give prescriptions for mouth correction and limit themselves to those for theoretical lengths obtained from the monochord. The reasons for this are to be sought in various causes. First, with the emergence of variable pipe widths, questions of length scale retired into the background. Because of the now variable width, making higher pipes narrower and lower ones wider than before, mouth correction was not as large as with a constant diameter. The problem of materials seems to have played a not inconsiderable part; the length scales of pipes made of lead or organ metal (alloys of tin and lead) can much more easily be corrected than the copper or bronze pipes of previous centuries. Later J. van Heurn[62] was to say however that exactness was not involved in scaling pipe length, because the right length was fixed at the voicing.[63] But the necessity of mouth correction was not

---

[61] His treatise was first published by J. Handschin in the Festschrift for Johannes Biehle (1930, p 40ff).

[62] De orgelmaaker . . . in Volledige beschrijving van alle Konsten, ambachten, handwerken . . . vol 19-21, 1804/05.

[63] As a result Van Heurn is able to give a prescription cleverly avoiding all circumstantial calculations for pipe length, i.e., the distance between 2 octave values (1 and $\frac{1}{2}$) is divided into $\frac{2}{3}$ lengths; the section thus obtained into 7, the remaining third into 5 parts. Hence the following octave series: C = 1, C sharp = $\frac{20}{21}$, D = $\frac{19}{21}$, D sharp = $\frac{6}{7}$, E= $\frac{17}{21}$, F= $\frac{16}{21}$, F sharp = $\frac{5}{7}$, G= $\frac{2}{3}$, G sharp = $\frac{19}{30}$, A= $\frac{3}{5}$, B flat = $\frac{17}{30}$, B= $\frac{8}{15}$, c= $\frac{1}{2}$. In cents (fundamental = 0 cents) the series would be: 0, 84, 173, 267, 366, 471, 583, 702, 791, 884, 983, 1088, 1200.

forgotten, as we can see from Bendeler,[64] Werckmeister,[65] and other writers; what was "added" to the width had to be "taken off" the length and vice versa.

I must refrain from giving and commenting individually on length scales in Georgius Anselmi (series: $1, \frac{8}{9}, \frac{64}{81}, \frac{3}{4}, \frac{2}{3}, \frac{16}{27}, \frac{128}{293}, \frac{1}{2}$), Agricola[66] (Agricola takes the pipe G at 16 ells long and gives the following series (without C sharp): $16, 15\frac{3}{16}, 14\frac{2}{9}, 13\frac{1}{2}, 12\frac{52}{81}, 12, 10\frac{2}{3}, 10\frac{16}{81}, 9\frac{13}{27}, 9, 8\frac{103}{243}$,[67] 8; with G as 1 this series runs: $1, \frac{243}{256}, \frac{8}{9}, \frac{27}{32}, \frac{64}{81}, \frac{3}{4}, \frac{2}{3}, \frac{413}{648}, \frac{16}{27}, \frac{9}{16}, \frac{128}{243}, \frac{1}{2}$), de Caus[68] ($1, \frac{24}{25}, \frac{8}{9}, \frac{64}{75}, \frac{4}{5}, \frac{3}{4}, \frac{32}{45}, \frac{2}{3}, \frac{16}{25}, \frac{3}{5}, \frac{128}{225}, \frac{8}{15}, \frac{1}{2}$), Kircher[69] (= de Caus), Mersenne,[70] Bendeler, Bedos,[71] although it is interesting to see how the scale precepts slowly abandon the pythagorean scale and move towards different ideal tempered series. But an examination of the sources with such an end in view lies beyond the scope of this work.

7

The practising organ-builder of that time used the scale precepts, rather as the modern organ-builder, rarely to produce pipes except to design a scale staff on which the values for the individual pipes were marked by colours or nicks. Since the octave progression of lengths (if mouth correction is ignored) comes to 1:2, i.e. the higher octave

---

[64] Johann Jakob Bendeler, Organopoeia, Quedlinburg 1690.

[65] Andreas Werckmeister, Orgelprobe 1681, 2nd edition: "Erweiterte und verbesserte Orgel-Probe" 1698 (Facsimile reprint by Bärenreiter, Kassel).

[66] Martin Agricola, Musica instrumentalis deutsch. 4th edition, Wittenberg, 1545, page 74ff (reprint in Publikation älterer praktischer und theoretischer Musikwerke, year 24, vol 20, Leipzig 1896). See also note 85.

[67] This should probably be $8\frac{104}{243}$.

[68] Salomon de Caus: Les raisons des forces mouvantes, Frankfurt-am-Main 1615, also in German (same year); Von den Gewaltsamen bewegungen . . .

[69] Athanasius Kircher, Musurgia, Rome 1650.

[70] Martin Mersenne, Harmonie Universelle, Paris 1636, and Harmonicorum libri XII, Paris 1648. In the latter work the pagination only goes up to the end of book 8 and starts again with the beginning of the 9th book (Harmonicorum Instrumentorum liber primus). This pagination is the one referred to in mentioning Mersenne's second work. I have not been able to see a work by Mersenne, "Traicté de l'orgue," in the British Museum (according to Eitner).

[71] Dom Bedos de Celles, L'art du facteur d'orgues, 1766-1778, 4 vols, reprint by Chr. Mahrenholz, 1936 (Bärenreiter).

always has half the measurements of the previous octave, it was enough to draw out the scales for the lowest octave and to determine the values of all octaves above using an equilateral triangle. On one side of an equilateral triangle the values for the lowest octave are given[72] and the points obtained are all joined to the opposite apex of the triangle by straight lines. When one of the other two sides of the triangle is intersected progressively in a ratio of 1:2 (i.e. $\frac{1}{2}$, $\frac{1}{4}$, $\frac{1}{8}$, etc.) and parallels are drawn to the first side of the triangle through these points, the straight lines leading to the triangle apex divide the parallels according to the ratios of the second, third and further octaves, depending on the number of parallels. Mersenne and Kircher, for example, give designs of this type.

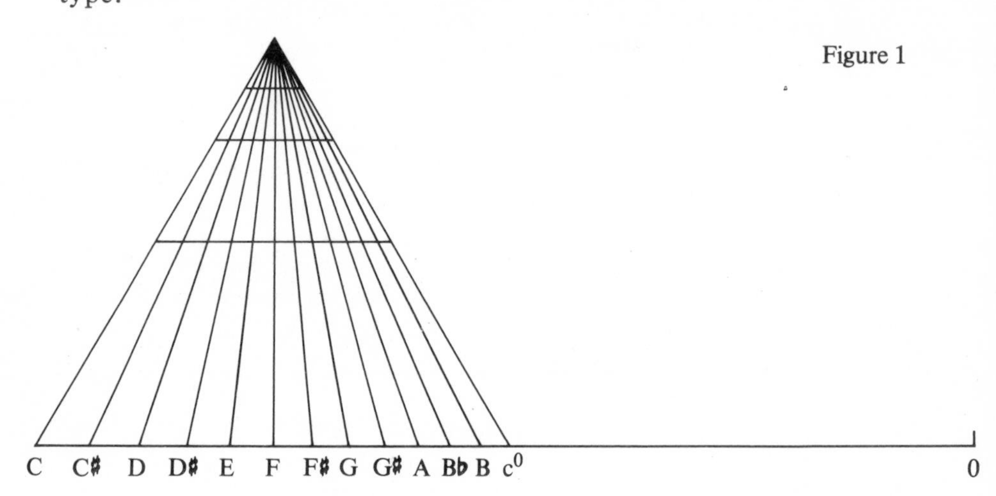

Figure 1

[72] Also starting with 0, corresponding to theoretical length. The geometric radiation rule is valid for any triangle.

DORDT COLLEGE LIBRARY
Sioux Center, Iowa 51250

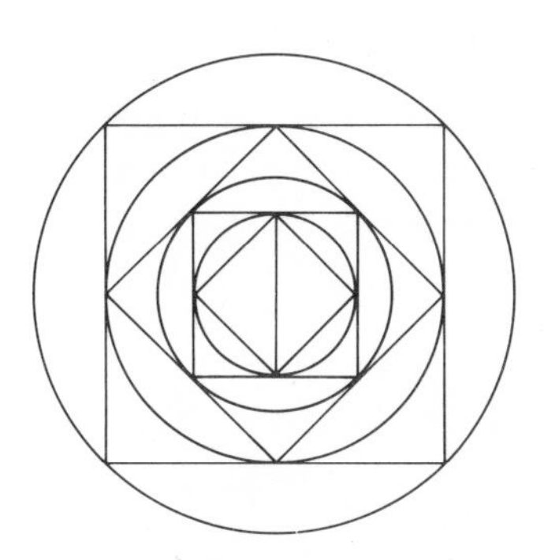

II Pipe Width

1

It has already been pointed out above that the width measurements of pipe series, as met with from the ninth to the twelfth centuries are the same for all pipe lengths.[73] Hence there was no scaling problem here for the medieval organ-builders. It is not known what actual width the pipes had, since most of the medieval organ-building tracts leave the determining of length and width to the organ-builder (*1, 6, 21, 22, 23, 25, 26, 27*) or have nothing to say at all (*2-5, 7-11, 20, 24*). However there are points of contact which allow us to reconstruct some of the width scales used then.[74]

Tracts *12, 13, 14, 16, 28, 29* determine the length of the standard pipe at 8 times the diameter value. The same length scale is supposed in *15* and *19.* Thus the width must be $\frac{1}{8}$ the length. Which length is meant? Of the prescriptions mentioned only *15, 16* and *28* (whose standard pipe can be identified by note) re-appear in the pipe series table.

The standard pipe for *15* and *28* is F in the Old French system, corresponding to A. The same point of departure was established for *16* above (see p. 18). In practice the length of a pipe a^2 is about 19 cm. The pipe diameter equal to the eight part of the length of the standard pipe is then about 24 mm. In the Berne anon. MS (*6*) the width of a pigeon's egg is given as pipe diameter, i.e. about 20-30 mm.[75]

---

[73] More detailed proof is given in Buhle, op. cit., p. 90.

[74] The results given below differ from details given by O. Walcker (Freiburger Orgeltagungsbericht, op. cit.) at several points.

[75] From E. Rey The Eggs of Birds of Central Europe, Gera-Untermhaus 1905, I,

2931355

The drawings given in two treatises of Gerbert (*17*, one drawing, *18*, two) do not take us any further either, since they are obviously not transferred from codices with exact measurements. In the case of *18*, at least, they were simply reproduced to fit the size of the space available opposite the text. There is also a drawing missing from *17* which was present in the source of this document.[76]

The codex from which Gerbert arranged the later version *18* is extant.[77] It provides another illustration, left out by Gerbert. It must first be observed that this codex dates from the 12-13th centuries, i.e. 200 years later than the original of the scale tract, but it was also written at a time when the directions given in *18* had little more of use to say to organ-building which meanwhile had progressed further. So it is not at all certain whether cod. lat. Monach. 18914 has the measurements of the original treatise. In fact the measurements of the original source seem to have remained unaffected in two illustrations; in the first,[78] with a free circle "latitudo", having a diameter of 12.5mm and a "longitudo" of 63mm (this is too small in practice), and, affecting the length scale, in the second at the end of *18* (Gerbert II, 282, below), since here the pipe length of 240mm was definitely drawn to fit the size of the space available in the codex. However a carefully executed drawing at the side of the Tegernsee Codex (wrongly placed by Gerbert, see note 78) is probably faithful to the original source.[79] The pipe length is given as 18.7 cm. This corresponds exactly to the length scale of a pipe a^2 calculated above (p.31). In this drawing the pipe diameter amounts to 24.5cm; here the drawing also agrees with the calculations examined earlier. The same width is provided by the drawing at the end of *18* (24mm diameter), though the pipe length can be shown as unreliable.[80]

---

p.393f, in German). Widths of eggs are given as follows:
27.5-29.2mm; wood pigeon, 25-30.5mm; ring dove and 20-24.2mm; turtle doves.

[76] Gerbert II, 223a has: "Primae ergo longitudo, sicut placuit domno Willehelmo, usque ad plectrum haec est," ("thus the length of the first as it pleased Dom Wilhelm, extends from here to the plucking point"), but this scale direction is left out in the later version.

[77] Codex Tegernseensis, now Codex lat. Monach. 18914.

[78] This comes after the words " . . . omniumque latitudinem huiusmodi esse volumus" (Gerbert II, 281b, line 15). The drawing reproduced in Gerbert at this point-"longitudo . . . secundum Eberhardum Frisingensem" (length . . . by Eberhard of Freising) – is placed elsewhere in the original.

[79] There is a caption: "Longitudo minime fistule scdm Eberhardum Frisingensem" (length of the smallest pipe according to Eberhard of Freising).

[80] The meaningless caption to the drawing in Gerbert II, 282 below – "Diametri

The drawing in *17*, (Gerbert II, 223) of almost the same design as that at the end of 18, with a diameter of 53mm, might seem impossible set against the results given, if it did not date from a later period. In the 11th and 12th centuries pipe width seems to have increased, probably because of the extension of the organ keyboard compass. The Schedula of Theophilus[81] gives 2" as pipe width, almost exactly agreeing with the drawing in Gerbert II, 223.

Compared to our modern organ scales the constant medieval width scale would start at the bottom with a diameter 1-1$\frac{3}{4}$ octaves narrower than today's "normal scale", depending on pitch. Assuming a range of 2-2$\frac{1}{2}$ octaves, the width achieved at the highest note would be about 1-1$\frac{1}{2}$ octaves above today's normal scale. A pipe series of this type could be made without any further difficulty.

2

It has still not yet been determined exactly when the transition was made to using pipes of different width within the same pipe rank. Hans Hickmann (op. cit. p. 70) gives evidence for varying pipe width scales in flue pipes by the 14th century. We do not know why the medieval fixed pipe widths were abandoned. Various factors probably contributed.[82] The need to introduce variable widths lay in the extension of the keyboard compass and, related to it, the difficulty of keeping the same pipe

---

parte VII" (in the 7th part of the diameter) is due to misreading.

In the Tegernsee Codex the drawing looks like this:

The diameter portions given ($\frac{1}{2}$, $\frac{1}{3}$, $\frac{1}{8}$) affect the working out of scales in *18*.

[81] Cf. Albert Ilg, Quellenschriften für Kunstgeschichte VII, p 304ff.

[82] It is not impossible that experimental considerations were involved. For so long had the note scale been achieved by pipes of the same width but different length, that it was not far-fetched to try the other way round, with pipes of the same length, but different width – it was already known from mouth correction that pipe width influenced pitch. The chapter "De organis componendis" (On the construction of organs) in Frater Walter Odington's (d. after 1330) tract "De speculatione musicae" (On Experiments in Music), reprinted in E. de Coussemaker, Scriptorum de Musica medii aevi novam seriem . . . Paris, 1864, p. 207f, is concerned with this problem. In my view this is a proof that variable width scales had become usual in flue pipe design by around 1300. It is of course impossible to experiment with the problem raised by Odington in practice, as Buhle (see op. cit., p.90, note 5) also recognised. Mersenne also deals with this question in detailed discussions.

width for more than $2\frac{1}{2}$ octaves. Another reason may be found in the search for a unified tonal colour throughout the whole pipe rank. As is known, the effect of the medieval fixed scale is to make the bass stringy and treble flute-like in tone; as soon as the change was made to providing several ranks of pipes in the organ, playable separately, where possible, an attempt was probably made to maintain the same tonal colour throughout a whole rank. A further reason could be that, as Gastoué (L'orgue en France, Paris 1921, p.35) has shown, variable scales were used as early as the 12th century in the design of reed resonators, and these were then transferred to flue pipe work.

But perhaps the decisive impulse towards the use of progressive width measurements lay in the fact that, having designed pipe ranks whose width was completely independent of the pipe length, now the opposite extreme was espoused and pipe width made to depend on pipe length throughout. The octave ratio of pipe width then – as with length – was 1:2.[83] While previously the length of one, usually the smallest, pipe was in a precisely calculated relationship to the diameter, now the same relationship between length and width was extended to all the pipes in a rank.

At the same time a greater freedom had been achieved in determining the length-width ratio, which previously was more or less standard at 8:1, calculated from the smallest pipe. For a long time $\frac{1}{4}$ of the length seems to have been taken for plate width ($= d \cdot \pi$). The length-diameter ratio was then about 12:1. Agricola, Mersenne and Kircher are all acquainted with this type of width calculation.[84] Mersenne also

---

[83] In organ-building practice the octave ratio of widths is normally called "scale"; it us usual to give the octave ratio of widths as ratios of the upper octave to the lower (i.e. of the smaller value to the larger), starting with the value of the smaller pipes as 1. While the old theorists obtained the ratio from values of the diameter or plate breadth, J. G. Töpfer introduced in his writings on organ-building the practice of starting with the pipe section, since the very frequently used square or right angle section wood pipes of Töpfer's day could be brought into relationship with round metal pipes only in this way. While the "scale" of pipe diameter is

$d_1 : d_2 = 1 : \frac{d_2}{d_1} = 1 : k$, the scale of pipe section is $\frac{d_1^2 \cdot \pi}{4} : \frac{d_2^2 \cdot \pi}{4} = 1 : \frac{d_2^2}{d_1^2} = 1 : k^2$

Via this highly unfortunate process of Töpfer, much confusion has arisen. By "width scale" I mean below always the simple ratio $1 : k = 1 : \frac{d_2}{d_1}$. The Töpfer scale $1 : k^2$ is expressly indicated as a section scale, wherever it is used.

[84] "experentia docet altitudinis rationem quadruplam optimi soni causam esse" (practice teaches a ration of $\frac{1}{4}$ the height to be the cause of the best sound) – Mersenne, Harm. libr. XII, p.116. It should be pointed out that even today $\frac{1}{4}$ the place breadth is considered the "normal" labium, $\frac{1}{4}$ the labium the "normal" cut-up.

gives the length-plate width ratios as 5:1 (for larger pipes), 5:2, 7:2 (for smaller pipes), 3:1, 2:1, 1:1, for stopped pipes 8:3 (lowest value), also 7:3, 6:1, 5:1, 4:1, 3:1, 2:1, 1:1. Kircher gives 5:3, 5:2, 4:1 for open pipes, 8:3, 7:3 for stopped (1:1 for the smallest stopped). These scales are naturally not to be used indifferently at all levels; the small ratio figures are more suited to the upper, the large more to the lower levels. The following table gives more details about this (octave ratio = 2:1 throughout, measurements are given in mm).

TABLE VI

Key	Length	Modern normal scale	*Diameter (in mm) with length : plate width ratio =*										
			6 : 1	5 : 1	4 : 1	7:2= 3.5 : 1	3 : 1	8:3= 2.67:1	5:2= 2.5 : 1	7:3= 2.33:1	2 : 1	5:3= 1.67:1	1 : 1
C^0	8'	155	138	165	207	236	276	314	331	355	414	497	828
c^0	4'	93	69	83	104	118	138	157	165	177	207	248	414
c'	2'	56	35	41	52	59	69	78	83	89	104	124	207
c^2	1'	34	17	21	26	30	34	39	41	44	52	62	104
c^3	1/2'	20	9	10	13	15	17	20	21	22	26	31	52
c^4	1/4'	12	4.5	5.0	6.5	7.5	8.5	10	10	11	13	16	26
c^5	1/8'	7.3	2.2	2.5	3.3	3.8	4.3	5.0	5.0	5.5	6.3	7.8	13
c^6	1/16'	4.4	1.1	1.3	1.6	1.9	2.1	2.5	2.6	2.7	3.2	3.7	6.5

Table VI shows that the 5:1 ratio is suitable for the low octaves of the 8′ and 4′ levels, but 1:1 only for the upper levels of the open 1′ or for small stopped pipes. The other ratios are compatible with the intervening foot-lengths in sections.

However only limited conclusions may be made from the measurement figures given about normal medieval scale values, which, apart from scattered indications (open, stopped, small pipes) are not systematized anywhere as to when and in what circumstances one or other of these ratios was used.

The 1:2 pipe width octave ratio at the basis of all these measurement figures re-appears in nearly all the organ theorists until the beginning of the 18th century. Martin Agricola,[85] for example, deals with this type of scaling at some length, also supplying a scale table.[86]

---

[85] Op. cit., reprint, p.271. The figures given by Agricola are converted here to the usual fractions; they are not altogether intelligible. E.g. "2 spans and 1 half third span" does not mean $2+\frac{1}{2}+\frac{1}{3}$; the last fraction refers to the previous $\frac{1}{2}$, thus $2+\frac{1}{2}+\frac{1}{6}$ is meant.

[86] See also above, p. 29.

Key	Plate width (in spans)	from 1 as base
G	4	1
G♯	$3\frac{51}{64}$ [87]	$\frac{243}{256}$
A	$3\frac{5}{9}$	$\frac{8}{9}$
B♭	$3\frac{3}{8}$	$\frac{27}{32}$
B	$3\frac{13}{81}$	$\frac{64}{81}$
c	3	$\frac{3}{4}$
d	$2\frac{2}{3}$	$\frac{2}{3}$
d♯	$2\frac{89}{162}$	$\frac{413}{648}$
e	$2\frac{5}{8}$ [88]	$\frac{21}{32}$ [88]
f	$2\frac{1}{4}$	$\frac{9}{16}$
f♯	$2\frac{26}{243}$	$\frac{128}{243}$
g	2	$\frac{1}{2}$

Mersenne also gives this scaling as normal, supplying an appropriate scale table (Harm. Univ., but see also p.52 below). Even J. Ph. Bendeler (op. cit.), whose opinion has some importance, as he was Arp Schnitger's stepson and a close acquaintance of A. Werckmeister, whom he calls his "very good friend," puts this method in first place, calling it the "best," the "easiest and most correct," and concludes:" This is and remains the only true basis of scaling and symmetry in musical proportions [i.e. in the proportions of the monochord, the octave ratio 1:2] . . . They [the pipes] are to be made both in length and width according to the musical proportions. This is taught by Nature herself, and cannot be denied by anyone who understands the nature of the musical proportions fundamentally."

Such passages, which at the end of the 17th and beginning of the 18th century are often linked to the disproving of ideas aimed at giving scaling a different basis,[89] do not give a clear indication of how far they

---

[87] Agricola gives $3\frac{35}{64}$, wrongly, i.e. $3+\frac{1}{2}+\frac{3}{64}$, instead of $3+\frac{3}{4}+\frac{3}{64}$, correctly.

[88] The length of pipe e is given as $9\frac{13}{27}$ spans. As the width is $\frac{1}{4}$ the length, the pipe width should be $2\frac{10}{27}$, with G=1, hence $\frac{16}{27}$.

[89] Bendeler, op. cit. "This business has up to now caused musicians and good organ-makers as many and wonderful thoughts as Mercurius of the philosophers did to the alchemists. It is commonly held that the scaling of pipes cannot and may not be carried out according to the musical proportions; thus some other basis is sought. Some think that the basis of scaling is to be found in solid geometry and not in the musical proportions, and therefore have not been afraid to attack the musical proportions as old and deceptive inventions of Pythagoras; it is much to be desired that this dispute be sorted out."

merely express a principle or, despite adverse utterances,[90] truly represent organ-building practice.

The application of the 1:2 octave ratio to pipe width[91] leads to tonal difficulties; it provides values too large for the bass, too small for the treble. The theorists always mention this scale, and so no doubt the reason is that, as with the other instruments, there was great concern to keep to the progressions of the monochord doctrine, which was so convincingly confirmed by pipe length, for width scales as well. As soon as the monochord ceases to be the basis of music theory, mentions of monochord width scale disappear from organ-building.

Another, variously stressed reason for choosing the 1:2 scale lay in a concern for evenness of tone; it was feared that this would be in considerable danger if the 1:2 ratio was departed from too much. Later on (p.48) we shall see that the theorists who held to this scale were not entirely wrong.

As long as the width scale stayed the same throughout the whole rank and pipe length was the only alterable measurement in a register, a scale staff or stick, on which pipe lengths were incised or marked, was all that was required in practical organ-building. But as soon as pipe width became variable the stick was no longer sufficient; the scale chart replaced it.[92] The design of the scale chart in all periods followed the principles of the co-ordinates system (see figure 2). The lengths of pipes are first marked in, as on the scale stick (see p. 29 above), on a horizontal axis from the point of intersection with a vertical straight line (O).

If the 1:2 octave ratio in the width described above is to be used, it is enough if the length measurement is marked out for a given pipe on the horizontal axis (OA), the perpendicular erected from the point thus obtained (A) and on this the pipe width chosen (plate breadth or

---

[90] "The practice confirms this. If this is not found to be so in practice and some of the sounds are too sharp, the fault is not at all in the proportions but lies in the fact that either the pipe according to which the scaling is done is too narrow and departs too much from the chorus width and nature of the sound (though the evenness is still there), or the organ-builder is not careful enough in the treatment of the small pipes . . . The musical proportions are still the only true basis for scaling and evenness in all pipe-work, flues (i.e. principals), reeds and flutes, be the flutes open or stopped, conical or cylindrical in shape, the reeds large or small; something more will be said about this below" (Bendeler).

[91] The octave ratio of pipe length is always the same at 1:2, irrespective of which temperament is used (Pythagorean, middle-tempered, equal vibration or other).

[92] As in earlier times, the pipe maker today as a rule still works by charts, not scale tables, as the measurements required can be drawn off the charts directly.

diameter) is supplied as ordinate (AB = w_5). A straight line is then drawn from the O point (intersection of both axes) through the end point of the ordinate (B). The ordinates obtained thus for all remaining pipes correspond to the pipe widths (w_1 , w_2 , w_3 , w_4 , etc. as for the abscissa of the pipe lengths).[93]

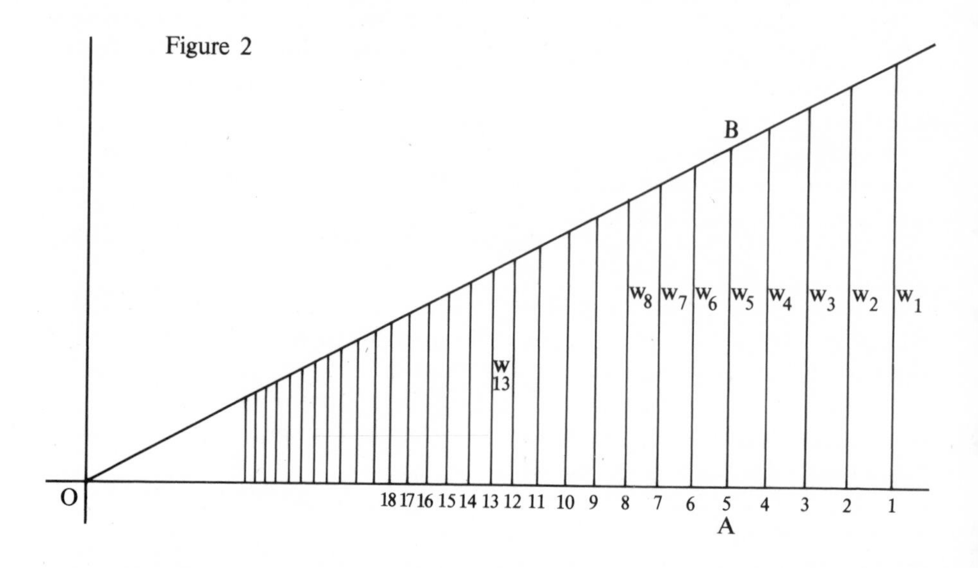

---

[93] For clarity only the ordinates for all C values of a pipe rank are inserted in the following illustrations. Besides the way given in figure 2 of presenting the scale chart, there is another met with in many cases, where the entries on the horizontal axis appear in the opposite direction (fig. 3). The diagrams are also more often turned through 90°, i.e. the horizontal and vertical axes interchanged.

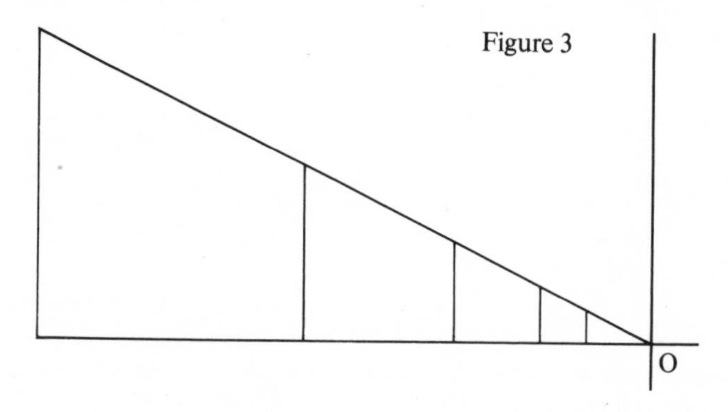

With the development of the scale chart, however, the absolute relationship of ordinates and abscissa very soon disappeared. The scale chart for large pipes would have been too unwieldy, because of the considerable length measurements on the horizontal axis. Thus the length measurements were reduced proportionally by half, to $\frac{1}{4}$, $\frac{1}{8}$, etc and only the pipe width was drawn at full size (or half size for large pipes).[94] In this way not only was a convenient scale chart provided but any given ordinates could also be determined as basic measurements of pipe ranks, and the widths for all the pipes of a rank were immediately available without having to construct a new chart. For instance, if the ordinate w_1 were taken for C^0 the octave values were given at w_{13}, w_{25}, etc; if w_5 was the starting point, there were the octave values w_{17}, w_{29}, w_{41}, etc. All these different forms of treatment were unimaginable when only the division of the horizontal axis was proportional to pipe length; the concept of the horizontal axis as an expression of pipe length simply vanished.[95] Thus the division of the horizontal axis in later theories could also be carried out following other principles than that of pipe length (see below).

3

Despite the defence by 18th century authors of the 1:2 scale progression in determining pipe width, organ-building practice had already begun to apply other progressions in part before 1500. The development of various register families also led of necessity to the evolution of a wide scale which did not markedly alter the tonal colour of a stop throughout its range and avoided abrupt transitions between the register families. This goal could only be achieved by freeing the determining of the octave ratio of pipe width from pipe length completely and thus appropriate values came to be used for this task.

One of the oldest of these numerical ratios seems to be that in which the half of the basic value is related to the double octave, not the octave, as for pipe length. The octave ratio is then $1:\sqrt{2}$. We find this

---

[94] For the length scales of the large pipes the scale stick came once more into use, as in the Middle Ages. This was constructed on the 1:2 octave ratio and showed appropriate indentations.

[95] A significant proof of this, for example, is the fact that Mersenne (Harm.Univ.) had already shown how the vertical axis could be constructed graphically (p.408f.) using the rules of a geometric series (i.e. semitone to semitone = $1:\sqrt[12]{2}$), although at that time even-tempered tuning, which alone would correspond to this division of the vertical axis, if it were a reproduction of pipe length, was not yet known.

ratio realized for the first time in a drawing of Burgundian origin from the 2nd half of the 15th century, now in the Paris Bibliothèque Nationale.[96] (MS lat. 7295, cf. Gastoué, chart 5). Measuring the photographic reproductions given in Gastoué produces the following values, for example:

c^0 :5.4 mm ∅
c^1 :3.8 mm ∅
c^2 :2.7 mm ∅

f^0 :4.7 mm ∅
f^1 :3.3 mm ∅
f^2 :2.3 mm ∅

These values, which could be multiplied as much as required, clearly show the application of the $1:\sqrt{2}$ octave ratio to determine diameter. The construction of this octave ratio in practice starts with the construction of the geometric mean between the two quantities a and $\frac{a}{2}$, or, differently expressed, given that the side of a square to the diagonal of the same square is $1:\sqrt{2}$, therefore $1:\sqrt{2} = \sqrt{2}:2$.[97] Thus the octave ratio of this scale is $1:\sqrt{2}$.

De Caus and Kircher reproduce this scale construction, providing a drawing similar to that in figure 4. Kircher gives the circles around the squares, de Caus uses only diagonals. De Caus also adds the design for

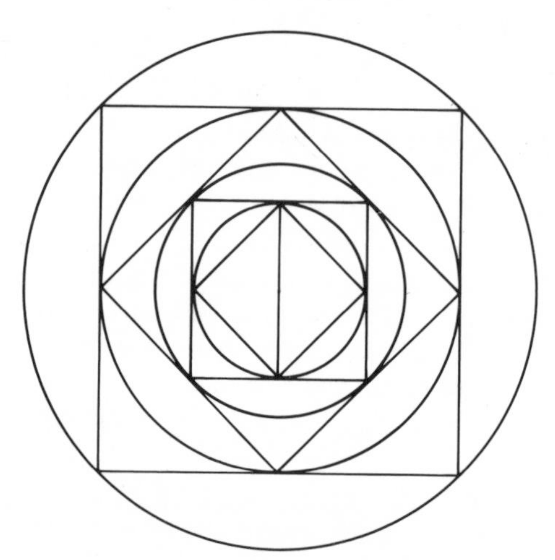

Figure 4

[96] also quoted by Walcker, Orgeltagungsbericht, p.44

[97] The $1:\sqrt{2}$ formula is found commonly in contemporary works, such as in W.H. Rivius, der Architectur fürnembste . . . kunst eygentlicher Bericht . . . Nürnberg 1558, p.11, not only organ-building.

quint ratios;[98] a right angled triangle is drawn, one of whose small sides equals the diameter of the upper octave, the other half the diameter of the lower octave; the hypotenuse gives the quint value (octave value to quint value = 3.2).[99] If the quint is constructed, by use of the quint circle all the individual notes of the octave can be obtained. Mersenne (Harm. univ. 398f) also gives the construction for a scale whose half width is related to the 2nd octave; the octave value construction is made by using the side of a square, as with de Caus, whose diagonal is the next lowest value, except that Mersenne, unlike de Caus, provides a correct scale chart which can be used in practice without qualification.

A pipe rank using the $1:\sqrt{2}$ width ratio comes close to the medieval fixed scale in as far as it has relatively narrow values in the bass and relatively wide ones in the treble. This scale is also thoroughly practical because it can be used for 5 octaves. Its possibilities for stopped ranks are expressly confirmed by de Caus. Mersenne uses it to design an open 16′ with a plate breadth of 2′6″ at C^0 (= 258.5 mm∅).

Nor need one stop at the ratio of the diagonals to the sides of the square; other symmetrical polygons could be used to design scale octave values. Thus in a regular hexagon the ratio of one side to one diagonal (not proceeding through the centre point) is as $1:\sqrt{3}$ (= 1:1.732), in a symmetrical pentagon side and diagonal are related to each other in the ratio of the golden section $[m_1:m_2 = m_2 : (m_1 + m_2)]$, i.e. as $1: \frac{\sqrt{5}+1}{2}$ (=1:1.618) etc.

Another line in scale design goes back to the diagram used by de Caus to obtain quint values, which has the ratio of a side to the diagonal of a right angle as its basis. Thus a diagram with side lengths 3 and 4 gives the octave ratios 3:5 or 4:5; side lengths 1 and 2 give the ratio $2:\sqrt{5}$,

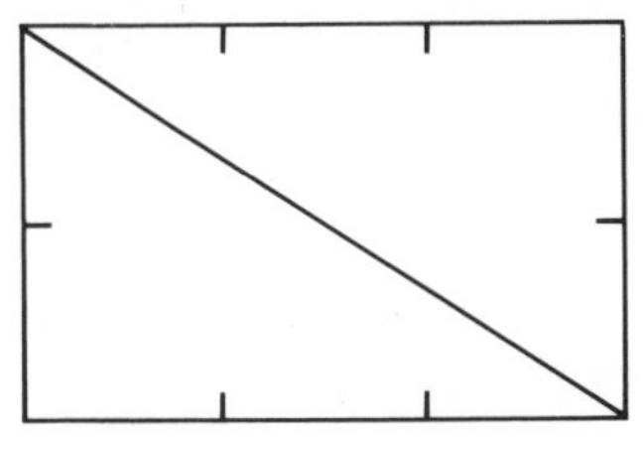

Figure 5

---

[98] De Caus gives no explanation of this drawing in the text, but its meaning is quite clear.

[99] If the diameter of the upper octave is taken at a, the diameter of the lower, following that stated above, is $a.\sqrt{2}$. The fifth value required is calculated following the Pythagorean formula:

$$q^2 = a^2 + \left(\frac{a.\sqrt{2}}{2}\right)^2$$

$$q = a\sqrt{\frac{3}{2}}$$

etc. The ratio 3:5 (=1:1.6667) produces a scale still nearer the Töpfer standard scale $1:\sqrt[4]{8}$ (=1:1.682) than the one using a pentagon (1:1.618) or hexagon (1:1.732).

Often the octave values of pipe diameters were sought not as above by geometric means, but the diameters of plate breadths of octaves were simply determined in their ratios to one another by numerical values alone. One of the oldest methods of this type is given by Georgius Anselmi.[100] The octave ratio here is 3:4, hence that for the double octave 9:16, a value which favours the bass width rather more than that of the Paris MS scale, providing very acceptable values. The values given by Anselmi for the intervening levels in the octaves are not usable, however (whole tone $\frac{17}{18}$, fourth $\frac{15}{16}$, fifth $\frac{11}{12}$[101] of the original value).

The results of Anselmi's calculations are as follows:

		for comparison:[102]
C : 1	= 1.000	1.000
D: $\frac{17}{18}$	= 0.944	0.953
E: $\frac{289}{324}$	= 0.892	0.909
F: $\frac{15}{16}$	= 0.938	0.887
G: $\frac{11}{12}$	= 0.917	0.846
A: $\frac{187}{216}$	= 0.866	0.806
B: $\frac{3179}{3888}$	= 0.818	0.768
c : $\frac{3}{4}$	= 0.750	0.750

At the beginning of the 17th century we find numerical ratios for determining width in the octaves more frequently in the theorists, which had certainly already been used in practice. These ratios are given; 4:7, 5:9, 3:5, 5:8, 5:7, 2:3. The scale chart shown in Praetorius, Syntagma II, p. 232, corresponds approximately to the ratio 5:9. This, and the ratios 4:7, 3:5 and 5:8 are mentioned even by Sorge as useful, and 2:3 is found in van Heurn (see p. 61). The ratios named give the following diameter values (in mm), taking a C 2′ = 50 mm∅ as standard:[103]

[100] Cf. J. Handschin, op.cit. p.41f

[101] There may be errors here; the fourth should read $\frac{16}{18}=\frac{8}{9}$, the fifth $\frac{10}{12}=\frac{5}{6}$.

[102] The comparison with an exact calculation of the intermediate values between C=1 and c=$\frac{3}{4}$ shows that the values for D and E give thoroughly acceptable results, but those for F and G are impossible, because they are larger than those for E. Here it seems that uncertain attempts are being made to get round the difficult geometrical means of design by use of arithmetic.

TABLE VII

	Diameter with octave ratio of										
	1 : 2	5:9= 1 : 1.8	4:7= 1:1.75	7:12= 1:1.714	3:5= 1:1.667	Golden section =1:1.618	5:8= 1 : 1.6	2:3= 1 : 1.5	1:$\sqrt{2}$= 1:1.414	5:7= 1 : 1.4	3:4= 1:1.333
C^0 8'	200	162	153	147	139	131	128	113	100	98	89
c^0 4'	100	90	87.5	85.7	83.3	80.9	80	75	70.7	70	66.7
c^1 2'	50	50	50	50	50	50	50	50	50	50	50
c^2 1'	25	27.8	28.6	29.2	30	30.9	31.3	33.3	35.4	35.7	37.5
c^3 $^1/_2$'	12.5	15.4	16.4	17.0	18	19.1	19.6	22.2	25	25.5	28.1

Of these ratios two gradually begin to have special signficance, 3:5 for flues and 5:7 for reeds.

The first ratio, used especially frequently in North German organ-building, can still be shown by taking measurements to day to have been used, where written evidence is lacking. It was effective well into the 18th and 19th centuries. The builder Johan Everhardt writes in a letter dated January 14th, 1770: "concerning the art of scaling; the first octave ought to be related to the second as with the principals and octaves 5:3 – which is the same as 200:120 but indicated as Gedackt, Flute 7:5" (see Bertil Wester, Gotisk resning i Svenska orglar, Stockholm, 1936, p. 58, note). In an 18th century organ-building treatise now owned by Fleck of Gottsbüren bei Hofgeismar the best scale for principals is given as the octave ratio 6:10 (=3:5). The octave ratio of van Heurn's standard scale for open pipes also follows the 3:5 ratio, although the rank scale itself is designed differently (see below, p.61).

The same is true of the ratio 5:7, primarily intended for reeds. How useful this last numerical ratio was for reed scales, especially tongue width, is shown in that Dom Bedos knew this ratio and used it as a unifying basic measurement. Bedos gives the drawing for standard reed shallots in plate 71 and on plate 7 the illustrations for the forms belonging to them. For simplicity Bedos always takes the same shallot for 3 notes, so that every 4th shallot comes at the beginning of a new octave. Measuring the individual widths from shallot 5 on shows that the ratio 5:7 is maintained unswervingly, as the following tabulation reveals:[104]

---

[103] The 1:2 ratio is also given for comparison.

[104] Taking measurements has shown also both how closely Dom Bedos keeps to the 5:7 ratio, and also how reliable the drawings in Bedos are here.

shallot no.	measurement	calculation with 5:7
5	19.6 mm	19.6
6	17.7 ,,	18.0
7	16.5 ,,	16.6
8	15.2 ,,	15.2
9	14.2 ,,	14.0 = $^5/_7$ of no. 5
10	13.2 ,,	12.9 = $^5/_7$ of no. 6
11	12.2 ,,	11.8 = $^5/_7$ of no. 7
12	11.0 ,,	10.9 = $^5/_7$ of no. 8
13	10.1 ,,	10.0 etc.
14	9.2 ,,	9.2
15	8.5 ,,	8.5
16	7.5 ,,	7.8
17	7.1 ,,	7.1
18	6.6 ,,	6.6
19	6.3 ,,	6.0
20	5.7 ,,	5.6
21	5.2 ,,	5.1

If Bedos were to use the 5:7 ratio for the low region of the 32′, over-large reed widths would be the result. Hence Bedos chooses a smaller octave ratio (4:5) for shallots A,B and 1-4, and brings 4 notes to each shallot:[105]

shallot no.	measurement	calculation
A	30.2	30.65
B	28.3	28.4
1	26.0	26.4
2	24.4	24.5 = $^4/_5$ of no. A
3	22.4	22.7 = $^4/_5$ of no. B
4	20.6	21.1 = $^4/_5$ of no. 1 etc
5	19.6	19.6 end of 4:5 ratio, start of 5:7

[105] It lies outside the scope of this work to discuss the very arbitrary practice of Bedos in the assigning of these shallot scales to the individual registers. It would be for a history of scaling mathematics to determine how measurements are obtained; this one example shows that the strictest discipline, not fancy, reigns here.

Even at the beginning of the 19th century we find tongue widths designed by the same means in van Heurn (vol. III, plate 27), fig. 17:

C 32′	=	29.5 mm	11.16
C 16′	=	20.3 mm	
C 8′	=	13.9 mm	
C 4′	=	10.0 mm	7:5
C 2′	=	7.8 mm	
C 1′	=	6.1 mm	
C $\frac{1}{2}$′	=	5.2 mm	7:6
C $\frac{1}{4}$′	=	4.8 mm	

The shallot widths of a house organ in van Heurn (fig. 18) are also constructed from the fixed 8:9 octave ratio:

C 8′	=	26.5 mm
C 4′	=	23.6 mm
C 2′	=	20.9 mm
C 1′	=	18.6 mm
C $\frac{1}{2}$′	=	16.5 mm

The reason influencing the use of such simple numerical ratios is quite clear. To make the scale chart construction simple, the obtaining of the octave ratio was sought by geometric means. This was very simple, as long as whole numbers were involved. But it became very difficult for the organ-builder, if not impossible, to reproduce, say, the ratio 1:1.732 geometrically. Thus the old organ-builders' self-restriction to simple numerical ratios is first explained by the state of popular mathematics in earlier times, of which geometry largely formed the basis.

A further reason,which should not be allowed to recede behind the first one, lies in the love of the old builders for particular ratios themselves. Number theories played a considerable role not only in the crafts. We need merely recall what an important place was taken by the discussions on monochord numerical ratios in the music theorists, further, that organ tuning was first a concern of theory, not practice or the ear, tunings obtained by ear were always corrected by mathematics towards the simple ratios; even equal temperament tuning was first an entirely mathematical and theoretical concept, mentioned around 1500 (cf. Riemann, Geschichte der Musiktheorie, p.329ff), not a practical way out of the "organ wolves" dilemma. Thus it would have been most exceptional if pipe length calculations had been closely related to the monochord calculations, numerical ratios had been completely excluded in pipe widths and only the values proven in practice were used. In fact the latter was not the case until about 1700 and only came into use when, with the general decay of the art of organ-building and the rise of a Romanticism averse to any numerical arts, the union of organ-building with the sciences of acoustics and instrument building was lost, and when, besides, viewed from the outside, many mathematical aids (e.g. the use of logarithms) came into organ-building.

To end this section a few words about scale chart design with the scales mentioned above. The loosening of the length-scale to width scale ratio in one scale chart has already been mentioned (p.39). As soon as width scale was freed from length scale completely, it became impossible – unless the drawing of curves were invoved – to represent length and diameter measurements on the same chart as abscissa or ordinates, even if reduced in ratio. A new division of co-ordinates had become necessary, based on the diameter scale ratio; thus the octave value of a pipe was found not by doubling or halving the basic measurement on the horizontal axis, but by a division corresponding to the chosen scale ratio (e.g. 3:5, 4:7, etc), and then as previously the ordinates of the remaining pipes were delimited by a straight line leading to the O point. Figure 6 shows a scale chart so constructed, based on the 4:7 octave ratio. Now the scale board also began to be diminished

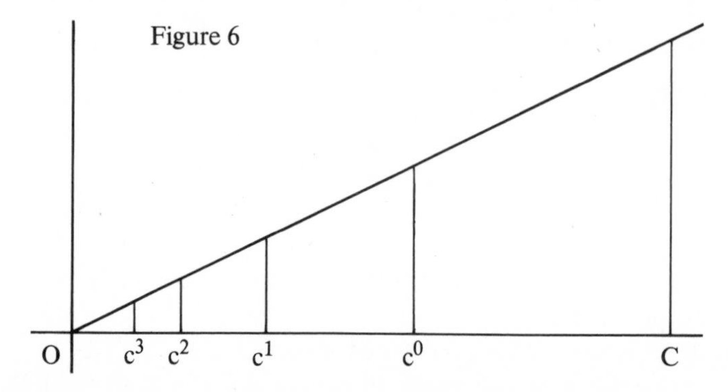

by drawing only the divisions of a single octave on the horizontal axis and placing the ordinates for all the octaves in the same field. Van Heurn, for example, gives a diagram of this type (fig. 7).

To obtain a scale using one of the methods in section 3, as with all the methods described hitherto, the width of a single standard pipe is required, beside the selection of a scale ratio. For the standard pipe the largest in the rank concerned is usually chosen, but sometimes the

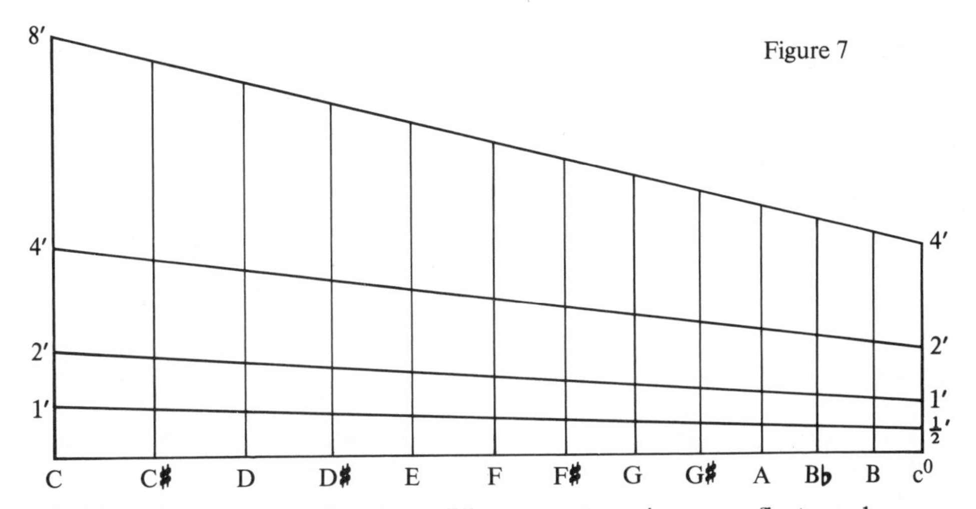

values of smaller pipes are used. When octave ratios were first used which did not correspond to the length progressions, the absolute width of standard pipes was still determined as a part of pipe length. Thus Anselmi, for example,[106] who gives the length: width ratio as 7:1, for a wide scale with penetrating tone. At $7\frac{1}{2}$:1 the sound is rough and loud, at 9:1, sweet. In Anselmi's view these measurements are only to be seen as relative values, which vary according to whether an organ in a big church or a house organ, to name the two extremes, is involved. But with these figures and similar ones, in contrast to the scales given above on page 33, the length : pipe width ratio suitable for the standard pipe should not be overlooked, since length and width are developed following different progressions. Hence it became usual later to give the width of the standard pipe simply in feet or inches. We have mentioned several such prescriptions. More can easily be provided.[107] Here also the more frequently met with data in organ-building and elsewhere on length and diameter of the largest pipe can be pointed out.[108]

---

[106] The Burgundian MS mentioned above also draws the pipes so that the length: diameter ratio at c^0 = 18:1, c^2 = 9:1.

[107] Cf e.g. Halle VI , p.226. The width of a 6″ long standard pipe comes to 6 grades (narrow), 9 grades (medium), 12 grades (wide), 14 grades (stopped). Further excursions into this area belong to a history of scaling, not of scale calculation.

[108] Cf the list in J.A.J. Ludwig, Gedanken über die grossen Orgeln, Leipzig 1762 (partly reprinted in the "Sammlung einiger Nachrichten Breslau 1757."):

Ulm Minster:	F32′ = 40″ (approx.306 mm∅)
Salemsweiler	D32′ = 4 spans (approx. 370mm∅)
Strasbourg Minster	D32′ = 1′4½″∅ (approx. 430mm∅)
Breslau, Maria Magdalena	G16′ = 14″∅(approx. 370mm∅)
" " "	A16′ = 1′∅(approx. 316mm∅)

4

In several of the organ theorists after 1600 we find mysterious remarks about the "Arcanum" (secret) of scaling. What is the case for this? Is the actual heart of scaling to be veiled fearfully from the gaze of all? Against this we know that the use of simple numerical ratios (3:5, 4:7) or the scales obtained by the help of diagonals in squares and rectangles, or the 1:2 scale following the musical proportions of the monochord, are discussed freely and with all clarity. The explanation of this apparent contradiction is to be found in the type of scaling which we are now to consider.

The scales calculated from the numerical values given in chapter 3 allow the organ-builder to shape the scale progression and relationship between bass and treble according to the demands made, by choosing an appropriate numerical ratio, and employing the scale progression for the tonal purposes apparent to him. As far as we can judge today this type of scale design was generally accepted for reeds, but with flues this was true only for a while, and then not everywhere Especially in the south and west does it seem to have taken no root; there the "natural" 1:2 octave ratio was held to with exceptional stubbornness. Above it has already been observed that this ratio can only be used effectively to a most limited degree. So as to be able to use it in practice, nevertheless, various ways out were found, all leading in the same direction. Basically another constant value or addition constant is added to each scale value calculated according to the 1:2 ratio, and thus the scale progression is corrected to make a practical standard scale. I have designated this method in my book on organ registers[109] as a fixed-variable scale.

First a word on the various ways of constructing these methods. The

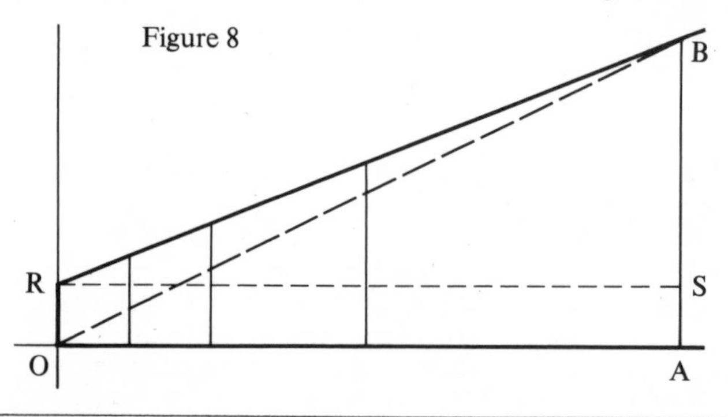

[109] Bärenreiter, Kassel, 1930, p.9

first (fig. 8) was to run the scale line's (from B) point of intersection with the vertical axis OR at a determined level higher, not through the O point.

The essence of the second construction (fig. 9) is that the theoretic width of the lowest pipe AT and the section TB is reduced and this value is added at the intersection of the scale line with the vertical axis OR. As

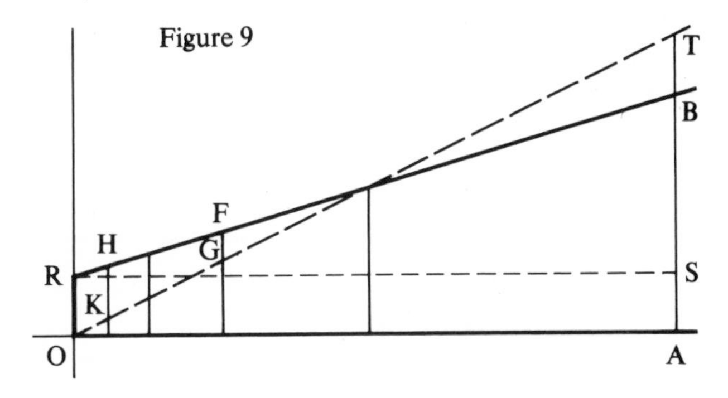

the division of the horizontal axis corresponds to the 1:2 ratio, FG is half TB. The new scale line always cuts the old (using the 1:2 ratio as basis) at the point giving the width measurement of the second largest octave pipe. A variant of this construction consists of measuring off the addition at the extension of the ordinate of the smallest pipe, so that KH=TB, not off the vertical axis. The displacement of the measurements given in fig. 9 is negligible.

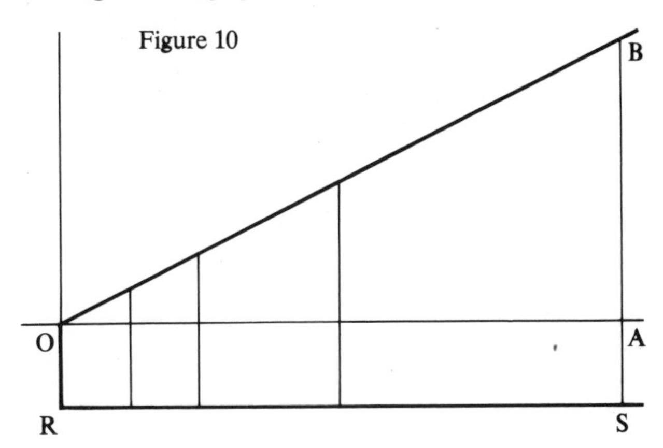

The third type of scaling (fig. 10) draws a parallel RS at a distance AS= OR to the base line OA of the scale constructed using the 1:2 ratio and measures off the scale values for each note from the parallels, not the base line. A fourth type of representation will be mentioned below (see fig. 14).[110]

All three constructions may be classed in two parts; 1, a basic 1:2 scale, represented in the BRS scale triangle (ABO in fig. 10), 2, an addition constant, RO=SA, added to each value found from the 1:2 basic scale as a constant value. The width of the lowest pipe then = basic value SB (AB in fig. 10) + addition constant SA. If the addition constant is taken as large the diameter increases, if as small, the bass is favoured over the treble. An example, using the 1:2 basic scale, fixing the basic value such that c^0=85mm, may clarify this:

TABLE VIII

Basic value	170	160	150	140	130	110	90
Addition constant	±0	+ 5	+ 10	+ 15	+ 20	+ 30	+ 40
C	170	165	160	155	150	140	130
c^0	85	85	85	85	85	85	85
c^1	42.5	45	47.5	50	52.5	57.5	62.5
c^2	21.3	25	28.8	32.5	36.3	43.8	51.3
c^3	10.6	15	19.4	23.8	28.1	36.9	46.6

With this scaling method it is possible to achieve any desired increase or decrease in scale values using one and the same basic scale, depending on the amount given as addition constant. This type of scaling, only applied to the 1:2 octave ratio, but occasionally used for other numerical ratios (e.g. 3:5), is met with in the theorists first in de Caus, then Kircher (here expressly for stopped pipes), and constructed using the first method described above. De Caus and Kircher part the horizontal axis according to the pipe length's ratios, i.e. with the 1:2 octave proportions; $\frac{2}{5}$ of its length (= $1\frac{1}{2}$) is given as the plate breadth of the largest pipe (F); for the plate breadth of the smallest pipe (c^3) its full length (= $\frac{1}{12}$ of the length of the largest pipe) is given. In this construction the addition constant is $\frac{3}{55}$ the length of the largest pipe; the value of the basic measurement for the lowest pipe thus amounts to $\frac{19}{55}$ the length of the largest pipe.[111]

---

[110] See below, p. 56

[111] The construction in the illustration differs from the explanation given in de Caus and Kircher. I have followed the text of de Caus and Kircher and discuss the illustration below (see p. 58).

The octave values are therefore the following:

$$\begin{aligned}
F &= \tfrac{19}{55} & &+ \tfrac{3}{55} = \tfrac{2}{5} \quad \text{pipe length}\\
f^0 &= \tfrac{19}{55} : 2 &= \tfrac{19}{110} &+ \tfrac{3}{55} = \tfrac{5}{22} \quad \text{"} \quad \text{"}\\
f^1 &= \tfrac{19}{110} : 2 &= \tfrac{19}{220} &+ \tfrac{3}{55} = \tfrac{31}{220} \quad \text{"} \quad \text{"}\\
f^2 &= \tfrac{19}{220} : 2 &= \tfrac{19}{440} &+ \tfrac{3}{55} = \tfrac{43}{440} \quad \text{"} \quad \text{"}\\
c^3 &= (\tfrac{19}{440} : 3)\cdot 2 &= \tfrac{19}{660} &+ \tfrac{3}{55} = \tfrac{1}{12} \quad \text{"} \quad \text{"}
\end{aligned}$$

The second type of scaling as expounded above, is found in the circle of the theorists Bendeler, Werckmeister and the writers after them.[112] The figure of Arp Schnitger is probably there in the background, Bendeler's father-in-law, who honoured Werckmeister's "Orgel-probe" (1690) with an introductory laudatory poem. Bendeler, who at first called the scaling using the 1:2 ratio the "most excellent" method, explains that the musical proportions can be departed from (pipe length or monochord) somewhat, "such that evenness is not noticeably hindered and one can also be quite certain about the height and depth of the notes." Bendeler characterises this scaling process as one "seeking convenience more than exact correctness." The construction follows the type given in fig. 9. From the width given at "70 scruples" (=21 mm) of the lowest octave pipe (calculated from the standard pipe[113]) "1 scruple 5-10" is subtracted[114] and half is given to the upper octave pipe.

The scale chart in Sam. Halle (Workshop III, chart VIII, no. 37), we find, is constructed in the same way. Even before Bendeler's work A. Werckmeister had presented the same type of scaling in the first edition of his "Orgelprobe" (1681), "because the organ-builders, concerning width, do not alter their pipe work using the musical radical-proportional numbers, but take a little away from the width of the deep or large pipes and are wont to add some to the smaller ones." Werckmeister adds, in the second edition of the "Orgelprobe" (1698), in which it is recommended "to read Mr Bendeler's 'Organopoiam' carefully": "Many organ-builders make laborious procedures out of scaling and a great mystery, only because they want to make themselves great thereby; but seen in the light of day this is about as difficult as the art of Columbus' egg . . . The main basis of scaling is that the biggest pipe

---

[112] E.g. Joh.Sam.Halle, Werckstätte 1764, III, p. 318, 320, 323, 348, etc.

[113] Described by Bendeler as the "previously given" or "known pipe tuned to choir pitch."

[114] as measurement shows, "5-10 scruples" is meant.

cannot be measured in width according to the musical proportions but something must be taken off the width, so that the evenness of the notes remains . . . Here is the secret, how much can be taken from the big pipes and given to the little, which can be achieved by arithmetic or mechanical means . . ." J. Adlung also (Musica mech. organ. 1768 II, p.78) presents the same point of view: "but notice that the organ-makers do not always order their pipes following the musical-radical proportions. They add something in the treble, so that the little pipes can be voiced better, but take away something in the bass, so that the sound becomes more pleasant; tuning also alters the proportion."

The third way of constructing fixed-variable scales, by drawing parallels to the horizontal axis and measuring off individual values from here is first mentioned by Mersenne, as the only form of fixed-variable scales at all, in fact. That Mersenne learnt this type of scaling in later years is shown by the fact that the same drawing in his "Harmonie Universelle" of 1636 is described quite differently in the "Harmonicorum libri XII" of 1648. In both cases a scale chart with the scale triangle OAC or OBC (fig. 11) is involved. Plate breadth OA is given at $\frac{1}{6}$, plate breadth OB at $\frac{1}{4}$ the length of the largest pipe (=1′). In both

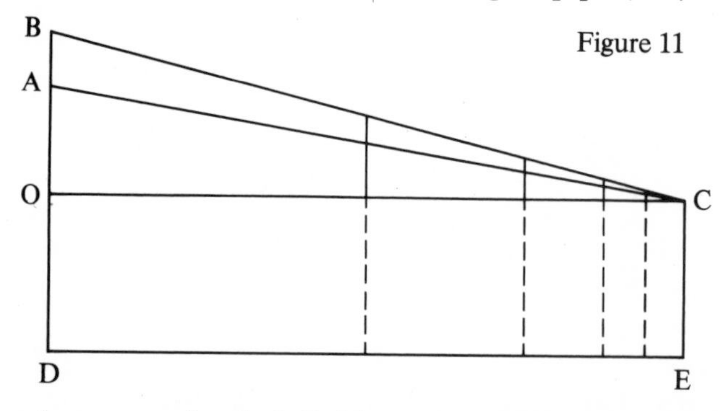

Figure 11

cases the scale progression is 1:2. The right angle added ODEC has nothing to do with the actual scale; it is intended for the registration divisions produced on the vertical axis by the various tunings given by Mersenne. Thus the relevant drawing in Harmonie Universelle (p.340) is also to be described. But in the "Harmonicorum libri XII" (p.129)[115] Mersenne includes the rectangle ODEC in the scale; the plate breadth is given as $\frac{1}{2}$ the pipe length, i.e. OD (=OB) is calculated in; for the narrower scale DA is used as width. Although Mersenne does not pro-

[115] The original text has some printing errors; in line 34 there should be χ instead of α, line 35 ψ instead of τ, line 36 γ instead of χ, line 37 η instead of φ, μ instead of π, and ξo instead of o.

duce further explanations, it is still clear that the scale found in the Harm. libr. XII is one with a basic value of $C^0 = \frac{1}{4}'$ or $\frac{1}{6}'$, with a 1:2 octave ratio and a $\frac{1}{4}'$ addition constant. Mersenne applies the scale to a 1′ Gedackt (2′ pitch), with these results:

	Wide scale		Narrow scale	
	Plate breadth in feet	Diameter in mm	Plate breadth in feet	Diameter in mm
C	$1/4' + 1/4' = 1/2'$	51.7	$1/6' + 1/4' = 5/12'$	43.2
c^0	$1/8' + 1/4' = 3/8'$	38.8	$1/12' + 1/4' = 4/12'$	34.5
c^1	$1/16' + 1/4' = 5/16'$	32.3	$1/24' + 1/4' = 7/24'$	30.1
c^2	$1/32' + 1/4' = 9/32'$	29.1	$1/48' + 1/4' = 13/48'$	28.0
c^3	$1/64' + 1/4' = 17/64'$	27.5	$1/96' + 1/4' = 25/96'$	26.8

Both scales increase sharply going upwards.

I have found this scaling method in old scale charts several times, often in a form allowing several parallels to the vertical axis, providing several scales on the same chart (fig. 12).

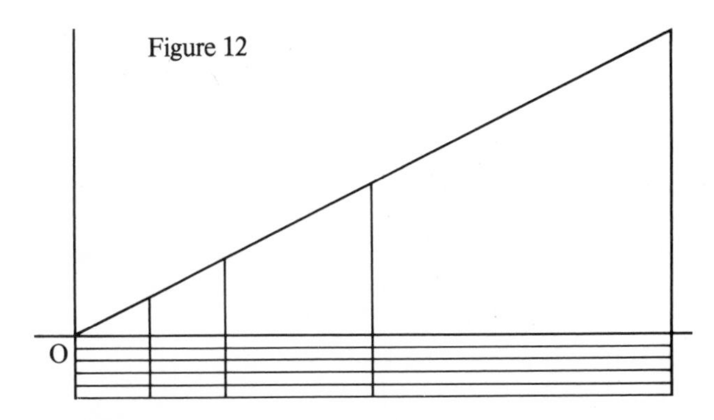

Figure 12

It has probably now become clear what is meant by the "secret". The musical proportions of the monochord are also basically to be adhered to here. The "secret" is nothing more than a slight corrective process, not altering anything fundamentally. The fact that not much was said about the "secret" should not merely be ascribed to workshop security. What would be the point of giving any particular addition constant? They alter for every register, even within a register, depending on specification chosen, room, etc. Even Bedos, who otherwise shows his hand completely, does not say anything on this topic. Probably this is because recording a number of addition constants would help the organ-botchers and copyists more than the real masters, not that this might be something that simply had to be kept secret. When Sorge[115a] later was to reject this type of scaling utterly and in so doing to criticise J.Ph. Bendeler and the secrecy of his time, two worlds are seen in confrontation, and their relationship cannot just be judged according to standards of "right" or "wrong."

As already mentioned, the method of designing the progression of a variable scale by including an addition constant was not limited to the use of the 1:2 octave ratio, however frequently this ratio may be found. Other fixed octave ratios can be chosen, such as 3:5, 7:4, etc., which may make it necessary to give the addition constant a negative value and place the parallels (e.g. in fig. 12) above the horizontal axis. Thus if the 3:4 ratio is chosen and an addition constant of –20 taken, the following values are the result:

$$119.0 - 20 = 99.0$$
$$89.3 - 20 = 69.3$$ (tr's note: given as 79.3)
$$67.0 - 20 = 47.0$$
$$48.7 - 20 = 28.7$$
$$36.6 - 20 = 16.6$$
$$27.4 - 20 = 7.4$$

The scale starts narrow in the bass, increases rapidly and falls off again at the top. It can be seen that using this scaling method allows ample freedom in designing the scale progression.

Variability is the characteristic of this kind of scaling, as compared with the constant scales described earlier having the same width ratio from note to note, octave to octave. The absolute ratio of widths to one another alters from note to note because the addition constant, which does not follow the basic scale progression, is added to these values and the values of the basic constantly progressing measurements cannot be matched with each other. Such a scale can only be arrived at in calculation if its basic scale is known or worked out from results.

This is specially important when old scales obtained from measuring are in consideration. We should simply not seek to analyse width measurements from old organs using our modern methods, e.g. octave section ratios. As an example I give the "Waldflöte 2'" of the Lüneburg St-Johannis organ, originally made as a Nachthorn. The diameters are: C=74, c=45, c^1=27.5, c^2=17. If this scale[116] is worked out the modern

---

[115a] George Andreas Sorge, der in der Rechen- und Messkunst wohlerfahrene Orgelbaumeister . . . Lobenstein 1773. Reprinted by P. Smets, Mainz 1932.

[116] As occured in the Freiburg Organ Conference report, p. 44.

way, the old organ-builder's octave ratio seems quite arbitrary, C:c=1:2.71; c:c^1=1:2.68; c^1:c^2= 1:2.62. In fact the 3:5 octave ratio and addition constant 1.3 mm are the basis of this register:

Pipe	Basic scale	True scale value
C^0	72.8	72.8 + 1.3 = 74.1
c^0	$72.8 \cdot {}^3/_5 = 43.7$	43.7 + 1.3 = 45.0
c^1	$43.7 \cdot {}^3/_5 = 26.2$	26.2 + 1.3 = 27.5
c^2	$26.2 \cdot {}^3/_5 = 15.7$	15.7 + 1.3 = 17.0

The Principal 4′ in Bedos cannot be given with the values C;c=1:3.6; c:c^1=1:3.2, c^1:c^2=1:2.7, c^2:c^3=1:2.2, either; the only valid scale here is the basic one, always, used by Bedos of 1:2 with a 5.72 mm calculated addition constant for the Octave 4′.

Pipe	Basic scale	True scale value
C^0	89.02	89.02 + 5.72 = 94.74
c^0	$89.02 \cdot {}^1/_2 = 44.51$	44.51 + 5.72 = 50.23
c^1	$44.51 \cdot {}^1/_2 = 22.26$	22.26 + 5.72 = 27.98
c^2	$22.26 \cdot {}^1/_2 = 11.13$	11.13 + 5.72 = 16.85
c^3	$11.13 \cdot {}^1/_2 = 5.56$	5.56 + 5.72 = 11.28

The scales of flues in Bedos are specially interesting in this respect. It cannot be discovered which of the three ways described above, Bedos used to arrive at these scales himself, since he only gives the pipe diameter of the largest (AB) and the smallest (LH) pipes, nor do his charts reveal anything about his methods of design. However the scale analysis mentioned above is easily obtained from these values (see fig. 13). The scale is arranged as a scale triangle RSB with a 1:2 octave ratio

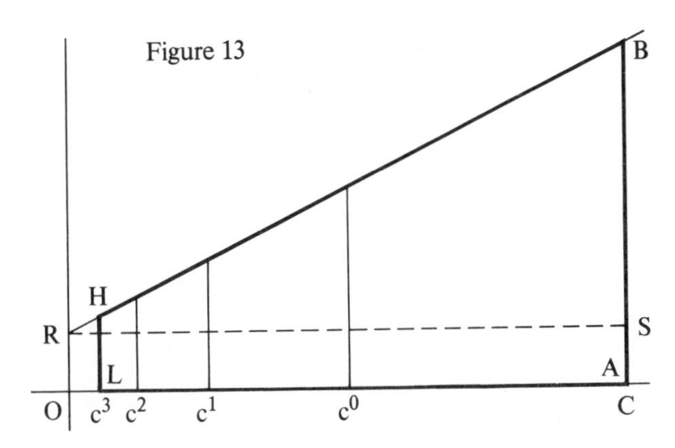

Figure 13

and an addition constant SA. All the flue scales of Bedos can be analysed in this way. Thus to construct the scales of Bedos only the basic value of the lowest pipe, whose scale progression is thus 2:1, and the addition constant are required.[117]

More details are given in the appendix about the scaling of Bedos. The fourth type of scale construction using an addition constant is based on the scale stick, not chart; its use had become normal for reed resonators since Bedos. This way of obtaining fixed-variable scales is only found with reed scales. Two examples are given in van Heurn. Van Heurn gives the circumference of the largest resonator for the construction of a scale stick for the width scale of a cylindrical reed and divides it into 52 parts (fig. 14). The circumference of the 8′ is found at the 36th part, the 4′ at the 28th, 2′ at the 24th, 1′ at the 22nd and the ½′ at the 21st.

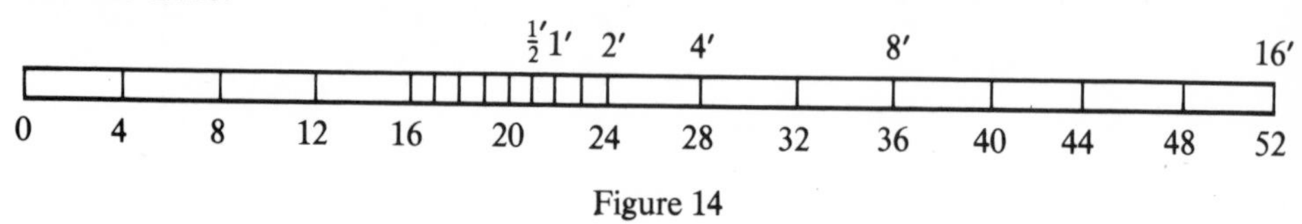

Figure 14

On closer observation we see that the true 0 point of the rank is at 20. From here the octave values increase to the right in a 1:2 ratio. The left side, 0-20, shows the addition constants:

Pipe	Basic scale	True scale value
C	32	32 + 20 = 52
c^0	32 : 2 = 16	16 + 20 = 36
c^1	16 : 2 = 8	8 + 20 = 28
c^2	8 : 2 = 4	4 + 20 = 24
c^3	4 : 2 = 2	2 + 20 = 22
c^4	2 : 2 = 1	1 + 20 = 21

The values for the notes in between can hence be obtained easily by geometric or arithmetical means. With conical reeds van Heurn divides the upper circumference of the lowest resonator, C 8′, into 48 parts and puts C 4′ on the 32nd part, C2′ on the 24th, C 1′ on the 20th, etc. Here we also find the use of the 1:2 octave ratio and an addition constant of 16 parts:

---

[117] I explained the scaling method of Dom Bedos to Fr Winfried Ellerhorst in conversation; Fr Ellerhorst then included it in his book, "Handbuch der Orgelbaukunst."

Pipe	Basic scale	True scale value
C 8'	32	32 + 16 = 48
C 4'	32 : 2 = 16	16 + 16 = 32
C 2'	16 : 2 = 8	8 + 16 = 24
C 1'	8 : 2 = 4	4 + 16 = 20
C 1/2'	4 : 2 = 2	2 + 16 = 18
C 1/4'	2 : 2 = 1	1 + 16 = 17

To construct a scale using an addition constant in practice, in contrast to the methods mentioned previously, either the addition constant or the value of a second pipe, usually the smallest, must be added to the width of one standard pipe as well, apart from the scale ratio. Adding the value of the smallest pipe is the most normal; see the details in Bedos, for example.

To make the analysis of fixed-variable scales using addition constants more easy, here are some formulae. If three octave values in sequence of a stop are known, a,b,c, a being the largest, c the smallest value, the addition constant will be:

$$v = \frac{b^2 - ac}{2b - a - c} \quad (4)$$

[118]

For width scale the formula is:

$$n : m = 1 : \frac{a - v}{b - v} = 1 : \frac{b - v}{c - v} \quad (5)$$

The basic value is a–v. If the known octave values are each 2 octaves apart, the same formula is used for calculating the addition constant. But the width scale is:

$$n : m = 1 : \frac{\sqrt{a - v}}{\sqrt{b - v}} = 1 : \frac{\sqrt{b - v}}{\sqrt{c - v}} \quad (6)$$

When v=0, the scale is fixed, without addition constant.

If the octave ratio of the basic values n:m in a scale with additon constant and 2 octave values a (large) and b (smaller) are given, the addition constant is:

---

[118] If 2b is $<$a+c, negative values are obtained for the numerators and denominators. To avoid this the following reworking of formula 4 may be used:

$$v = \frac{ac - b^2}{a+c - 2b}$$

$$v = \frac{b \cdot m^z - a \cdot n^z}{m^z - n^z} \quad (7)$$

where z = the number of octaves between a and b. This formula simplified is:

$$v = \frac{b \cdot k^z - a}{k^z - 1} \quad (8)$$

where $k = \frac{m}{n}$. If n:m = 1:2 (as in Bedos), ∴ k = 2, thus

$$v = \frac{b \cdot 2^z - a}{2^z - 1} \quad (9)$$

5

An interesting development of the scale with addition constant is also found in the sources. As indicated above, the bass, and particularly the treble are affected in their width as against the middle area, in 1:2 ratio fixed-variable scales using addition constants. To counteract this, a bend was made in the scale line, usually where the second octave begins from below, favouring the middle area (fig. 15).

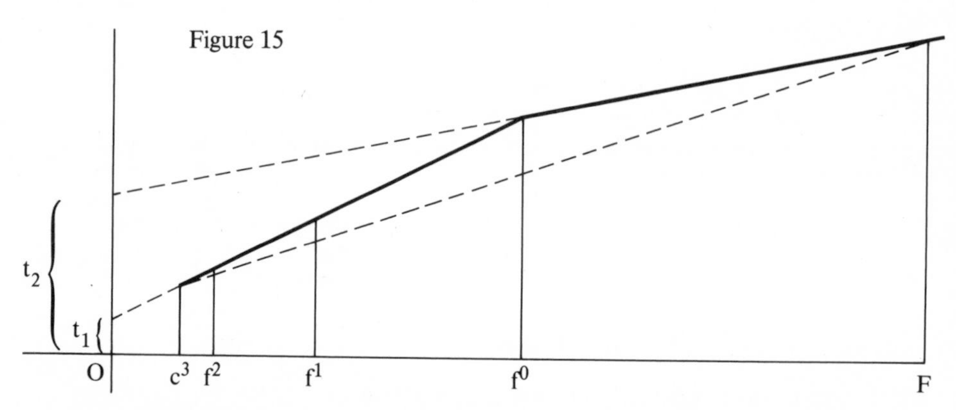

This scale construction can also be analysed such that the addition constant changes through the rank. Thus in fig. 15 the addition constant t_2 would be valid from F-f^0, t_1 from f^0-c^3.

The first construction of this type is shown in de Caus [119] (and later

[119] See p. 51 on the passage in de Caus. Kircher does not explain the bend in the scale line either.

by Kircher, given as “systema iuxta Causium”). This is the same as the scale of a rank given above (see p. 51) where F = $\frac{2}{5}$, c^3 = $\frac{1}{12}$ the pipe length. In the de Caus illustration the first octave value, f^0, is given at $\frac{2}{7}$ the pipe length, introducing a sharp rise in this value against the standard progression. The following octave values are thus determined by the size of f^0. This series is the result (1= pipe length):

Pipe	Basic diameter value	True diameter	Addition constant
F	$^8/_{35}$	$^8/_{35} + ^6/_{35} = ^{14}/_{35} = ^2/_5$ l	$^6/_{35}$ l (F, f^0)
f^0	$^8/_{35} : 2 = ^4/_{25}$ $^{17}/_{70}$	$^4/_{35} + ^6/_{35} = ^{10}/_{35} = ^2/_7$ l $^{17}/_{70} + ^3/_{70} = ^{20}/_{70} = ^2/_7$ l	
f^1	$^{17}/_{70} : 2 = ^{17}/_{140}$	$^{17}/_{140} + ^3/_{70} = ^{23}/_{140}$ l	$^3/_{70}$ l (f^0–c^3)
f^2	$^{17}/_{140} : 2 = ^{17}/_{280}$	$^{17}/_{280} + ^3/_{70} = ^{21}/_{280}$ l	
c^3	$(^{17}/_{280} : 3) \cdot 2 = ^{17}/_{420}$	$^{17}/_{420} + ^3/_{70} = ^{35}/_{420} = ^1/_{12}$ l	

If this series (II) is compared with that calculated on p. 51 (I), the improvement in the middle area in II becomes clear:

	I	II
F	d = 0.400 ·l	d = 0.400 ·l
f^0	d = 0.227 ·l	d = 0.286 ·l
f^1	d = 0.143 ·l	d = 0.164 ·l
f^2	d = 0.098 ·l	d = 0.103 ·l
c^3	d = 0.083 ·l	d = 0.083 ·l

Later we also find this type of scale construction again in Dom Bedos. The plein-jeu fourniture and cymbale scale is shown with a bend making the scale line of the low octave run flatter than the high ones, “to reduce the width of the first octave pipes.” (Bedos, p.74). Thus, in the wide plein-jeu scale the addition constant for the C-B 4′ low octave is 12.0mm, for the rest, only 4.2mm. The narrow plein-jeu scale, meant for the back positive, begins at C 2′ and continues with an addition constant of 3.3mm, but has no bend in the scale line.

Bendeler also has this method, as a way of dealing with the difficulties produced by the standard fixed-variable scale with addition constant. “Whether one can scale very easily [i.e. with addition constant] . . . I cannot conceal that since the lower keys [notes] lack width, but the upper ones have too much, if a great amount were taken away from the descending octave much unevenness would be felt. Therefore I will now reveal the truly undeceiving and incontrovertible basis of deduction scaling."

Bendeler's scale chart is constructed similarly to that for fixed-variable scales (see p. 49 (fig. 9) and p. 51 above). The width of the standard pipe is erected as an ordinate in M on the horizontal axis divided in the 1:2 octave ratio and the scale line OU is drawn (fig. 16).

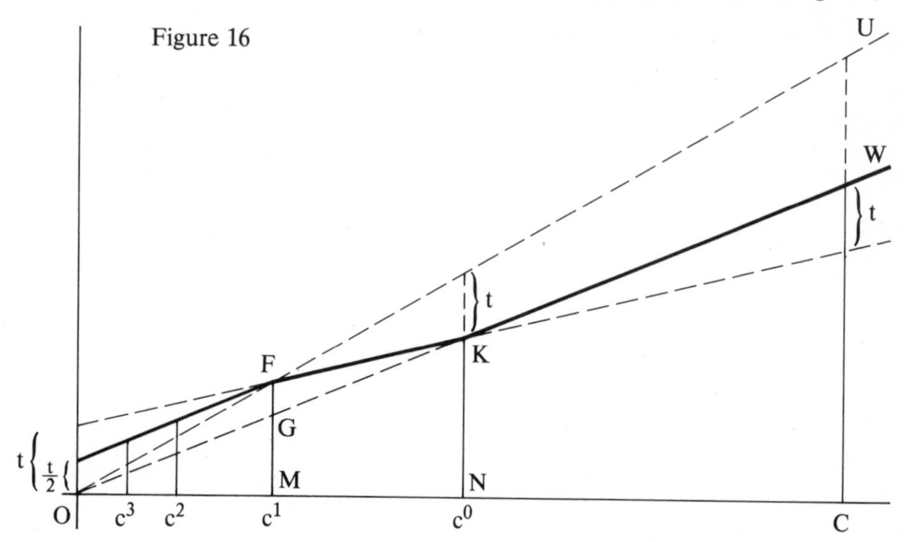

The "deduction" t (see p. 51 above) is taken from the ordinate of the next lowest octave, N, calculated from the standard pipe, and the scale line OW is constructed to the newly obtained value. The section FG ($=\frac{t}{2}$) is taken from the O axis and the endpoint joined to F and F to K. The scale thus formed has 2 bends. If a= the width of the standard pipe, the increasing octave values 2a−t, 4a−2t, 8a−4t, 16a−8t, etc, reduced by the deduction but otherwise following the 1:2 octave ratio, are the result for the low octaves. This measurement calculation gives greater width in the bass than a fixed-variable scale, as sought by Bendeler, which would have 2a−t, 4a−3t, 8a−7t, 16a−15t, etc, as octave values. The pipes between a and the next octave below are constructed from the 1:2 scale + addition constant t; thus the pipe width increases, to the advantage of the middle area. The octaves above only receive $\frac{t}{2}$ as addition constant, so that "the upper heights do not receive too [119a]

[119a] When the section MG is given as g (thus $a=g+\frac{t}{2}$), the octave series becomes, starting with the largest pipe, 32g, 16g, 8g, 4g, 2g, $g+\frac{t}{2}, \frac{g}{2}+\frac{t}{2}, \frac{g}{4}+\frac{t}{2}, \frac{g}{8}+\frac{t}{2}, \frac{g}{16}+\frac{t}{2},$ etc.

much." In the introduction to his work, Bendeler describes this method as: "very good in practice too, because the upper notes, without noticeable loss of evenness obtained a delicate sharpness by this addition, so that they do not squeak like young mice."

A similar scaling method, changing the addition factor through the progression, is given by van Heurn. This is a scale with a 3:5 (for open pipes) or 2:3 (for stopped) octave ratio, but with the horizontal axis of the scale stick executed according to the 1:2 ratio, not those given. This construction (fig. 17) produces a scale line falling off more towards the top and having a bend at each C.

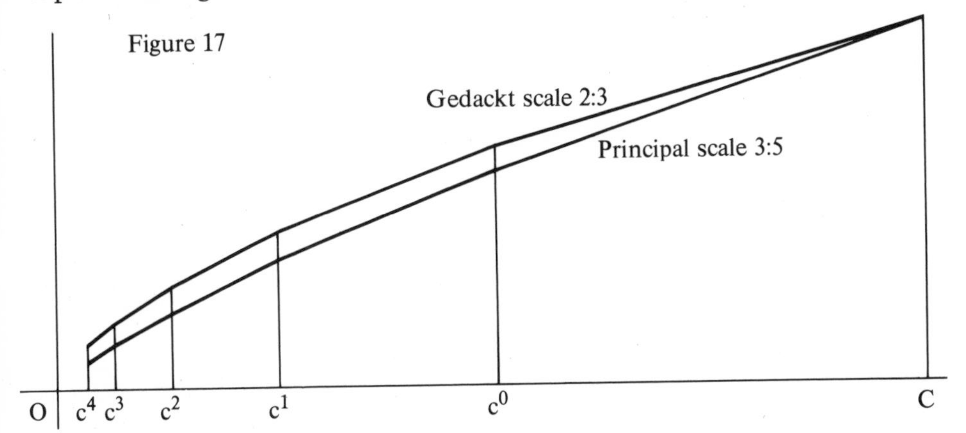

Figure 17

(van Heurn draws this scale in the form given on p. 47). It can be so organized that the changing addition constant is $\frac{a}{5}$ when the scale is 3:5, $\frac{a}{3}$ at 2:3 scale, where a= C value of the octave. Thus the addition factor is reduced from octave to octave, depending on the basic scale. The departures of this fixed variable scale from the standard 3:5 or 2:3 scale are limited, and never concern the C values, besides.

The scales considered hitherto are all based on geometrical series with the extra element of an addition constant in the scales given in chapters 4 and 5. The departure from the strict form of the geometric series is the greater, the more the addition constant is in relation to the corresponding basic value. Arithmetical series also have an important part in the scaling methods of the old builders, as well as geometric. These series can be applied where the octave ratio produces such a low value, as with determining reed stop measurements, even reeds themselves, that this value can be approximately represented by an arithmetical series and can also dispense with the use of a geometrical series in constructing a scale chart.[120]

Such series are first encountered in Mersenne (Harm. univ. and Harm. libr. XII), to construct reed shallots. Length at 8′ C is 4″, at $\frac{1}{2}$′ C a quarter of this, i.e. 1″. The difference, 3″ , is divided into 15 parts, of which each part represents $\frac{1}{20}$ the reed length at 8′ C; each part is used for 3 notes, without c♯ in the lowest octave. The following series results:

C, D, D♯	:	20 parts	~	4″
E, F, F♯	:	19 ”	~	$3\frac{4}{5}$″
G, G♯, A	:	18 ”	~	$3\frac{3}{5}$″
B♭, B, c	:	17 ”	~	$3\frac{2}{5}$″
c♯, d, d♯	:	16 ”	~	$3\frac{1}{5}$″
		etc, to		
$b♭_2$, b_2, c_3	:	5 ”	~	1″

The same progression is given for shallot width, with 8′ values =1″ and its $\frac{1}{2}$′ value = $\frac{1}{4}$″.

Kircher gives the same construction for his “zooglossa”.[121] Mersenne give 3″ (for 8′ C) and $\frac{2}{3}$″ for $\frac{1}{2}$′ C (Harm. univ, and Harm. libr. XII) as the vox humana reed scale. The internal distance, $\frac{7}{9}$ the value of 8′ C, is divided into 11 parts, each $\frac{7}{99}$ of 8′ C; one is used for 4 notes C♯ is also missing here, thus giving this series:

---

[120] The following example may serve for comparison:

Geometrical series (5:6 ratio)	Arithmetical series
24.0	24.0
× 6/5 = 28.9	+ 7 2 = 31.2
× 6/5 = 34.7	+ 7 2 = 38.4
× 6/5 = 41.6	+ 7 2 = 45.6
× 6/5 = 50.0	+ 7 2 = 52.8
× 6/5 = 60.0	+ 7 2 = 60.0

[121] On this see my “Orgelregister,” p. 166.

C, D, D#, E	: $\frac{99}{99}$	~	3″
F, F#, G, G#	: $\frac{92}{99}$	~	$2\frac{26}{33}$″
A, Bb, B, c	: $\frac{85}{99}$	~	$2\frac{19}{33}$″
c#, d, d#, e	: $\frac{78}{99}$	~	$2\frac{4}{11}$″
	etc., to		
a^2, bb^2, b^2, c^3	: $\frac{22}{99}$	~	$\frac{2}{3}$″

Tongue width is standardised at $\frac{3}{8}$″ for 8′ C, $\frac{3}{16}$″ for $\frac{1}{2}$′ c. The widths decrease by $\frac{1}{5}$ the original breadth, every 8 notes, producing the following series:

C-G#	: $\frac{3}{8}$″	= 0.3750″
A-e^0	: $\frac{27}{80}$″	= 0.3375
f^0-c^1	: $\frac{24}{80}$″	= 0.3000″
$c\#^1$-$g\#^1$	: $\frac{21}{80}$″	= 0.2625″
a^1-e^2	: $\frac{18}{80}$″	= 0.2250″
f^2-c^3	: $\frac{3}{16}$″	= 0.1875″

Kircher gives the same scale.

The length of the vox humana tops[122] is also represented in arithmetical sequence; in both works Mersenne gives a top length of $\frac{1}{2}$′ for the 8′ C^0 of a cylindrical vox humana with a conical base, of which $\frac{8}{15}$ goes to the conical base, which remains the same, while the cylindrical top takes up $\frac{7}{15}$ of the total length at C^0. The length of the cylinder top reduces every 4 notes by $\frac{7}{220}$ the whole length of the top at C^0. The series is then:

C, D, D#,E	: $\frac{220}{220}$	~	$\frac{1}{2}$′
F, F#, G, G#	: $\frac{213}{220}$	~	$\frac{213}{440}$′
A, Bb, B, c	: $\frac{206}{220}$	~	$\frac{206}{440}$′
c#, d, d#, e	: $\frac{199}{220}$	~	$\frac{199}{440}$′
f, f#, g, g#	: $\frac{192}{220}$	~	$\frac{192}{440}$′
	etc, to		
a^2, bb^2, b^2, c^3	: $\frac{143}{220}$	~	$\frac{143}{440}$′

Kircher also gives the same scale in this form.

---

[122] Their widths are the same throughout the series.

For a vox humana with conical resonators the length of the largest pipe is given by Mersenne in Harm. univ. as 6″, the smallest as $3\frac{1}{2}$″. The $2\frac{1}{2}$″ difference is divided into 15 parts of $\frac{1}{6}$″, of which one is used for every 3 notes. This series is:

C, D, D#	: $\frac{36}{6}$	~ 6″
E, F, F#	: $\frac{35}{6}$	~ $5\frac{5}{6}$″
G, G#, A,	: $\frac{34}{6}$	~ $5\frac{2}{3}$″
B♭, B, c	: $\frac{33}{6}$	~ $5\frac{1}{2}$″
c#, d, d#	: $\frac{32}{6}$	~ $5\frac{1}{3}$″
e, f, f#	: $\frac{31}{6}$	~ $5\frac{1}{6}$″
	etc, to	
b♭², b², c³	: $\frac{21}{6}$	~ $3\frac{1}{2}$″

Bedos also uses arthmetical progressions to obtain the 4 crumhorn scales (plate 29) given by him. Here are the diameters of the scales I and IV, in mm:

	I	IV
C	55.0	32.4
c^0	47.4	29.1
c^1	39.7	25.8
c^2	32.1	22.5
C-C difference	7.6	3.3

7

With Georg Andreas Sorge begins a new era of scaling mathematics. The musical proportions, which had been the basis of scale calculations for nearly a millenium as the expression of a particular musical point of view, have nothing more to say; by removing the proportions from music, equal temperament had also destroyed its theoretical significance as the "natural" basis of instrument design and tone.

Extremely conscious of his advanced learning, Sorge entered the field against Bendeler, the last classic representative of the old system. Bendeler had written "something which I will leave, whether it be good or bad. This treatising is not expensive and I do not want to cause its author any debts. But what he has written about scaling the width and length of a pipe is wrong, dark and unsure." Now come blow upon blow against Bendeler, Werckmeister and Adlung, who have "taught wrongly." Even the numerical ratios, which had had great importance in constructing organ scales, previously, could now be abandoned; the means of calculation with logarithms which had meanwhile gained wider currency offered the possibility of giving up calculation using whole numbers: "Indeed, to determine octave width the ratios 4:7, 5:9 and 3:5 as well as 5:8 can be given, but this leads to a vicious circle and makes calculating and measuring out unnecessarily difficult" (Sorge, preface, see above, note 115a).

Sorge's scaling method amounts to keeping the 1:2 ratio, which was the only one of the old proportions to survive in even-tempered tuning, not for the octave, but another interval, the ninth: "the width is not to be sought in the length; it must be so determined that the 1:2 ratio is given to the ninth, or the major or minor tenth." This is the type of scaling meant, when the phrase "half goes to this pipe or that one" is used in organ-building today.[123]

Of the three scales given by Sorge (table IX, nos 1-3), the "ninth-scale" is to be taken as standard. The proportions in between for individual notes are calculated as geometric series.

TABLE IX

	No.	The 1:2 diameter ratio corresponds to the interval of a:	Diameter octave ratio (width scale)	Cross-section octave ratio (cross-section scale)
Sorge	1	Ninth (c^0 : d^1)	1 : 1.811	1 : 3.281
	2	Minor tenth (c^0 : $e\#^1$)	1 : 1.741	1 : 3.032
	3	Major tenth (c^0 : e^1)	1 : 1.682	1 : 2.828
Topfer	4	Eleventh (c^0 : f^1)	1 : 1.631	1 : 2.661
	5	Diminished twelfth (c^0 : $f\#^1$)	1 : 1.587	1 : 2.519

J. G. Töpfer later returned to Sorge's type of scaling[124] and brought it into general use, although his starting point was different. Töpfer

[123] This has remained unimportant to mathematical determining of the scale. Both diameter and cross section scale have always been ascertained by the octave ratio. Nor is Sorge entirely without precedent. Bedos, for example, calculates the reed scale theoretically according to the 5:7 octave ratio, but the measurements thus obtained are so allotted to the individual notes that in practice the 5:7 ratio does not come at the octave.

[124] Orgelbaukunst, Weimar 1833; Erster Nachtrag zur Orgelbaukunst, Weimar 1834; Lehrbuch der Orgelbaukunst, Weimar, 1835.

abandons the ninth-scale. But his 1:3 cross-section scale corresponds almost exactly to the minor tenth scale (table IX, no 2), and Töpfer's standard, cross-section scale of $1:\sqrt[2]{8}$ (=1:2.8284) corresponds to the major tenth scale (table IX, no 3) in Sorge. Töpfer also adds two furthe scales (table IX, nos 4 +5).

Töpfer's achievement was to give the $1:\sqrt{8}$ scale a theoretical foundation. This scale itself was not invented by Töpfer; it was already known at the beginning of the 18th century, as became clear above.

Carl Kützing[125] developed the principle introduced by Sorge's work more logically than any one. A 16′ C is constructed "of such a width that the sound is as perfect as possible." The same is done with a $\frac{1}{4}$′ C pipe. "When these two sizes have been determined, the intervening ones making up a geometric series, can easily be found by use of logarithms.' The octave ratio found by Kützing in practice is 1:1.64. This value approximates to Töpfer's eleventh-scale (table IX, no 4). Kützing constructs reed resonators, tongue thicknesses (32′ C is given as 1.5 lines – 3mm approx., $\frac{1}{4}$′ C, 0.1 lines = 0.2 mm approx; the octave ratio is 1:1.472, i.e. approx, 2:3), etc.

8

All the scale ratios considered hitherto, except those based on arithmetical series mentioned in chapter 6, can be derived from the basic formula

$$d_x = (d_1 - v) \cdot \left(\frac{n}{m}\right)^{\frac{x-1}{z-1}} + v \tag{10}$$

For simplicity it is assumed that tempered tuning is used, so that the scales, apart from v, are developed in geometric series. To explain this formula: d_x is the width of the pipe sought on a given key, d_1 is the width of a given pipe, $d_1 > d_x$.[126] The number of keys, in semitones, from d_1-d_x inclusive is x. Thus if the width of C^0 is given, and the width of f^0 is sought, x = 18. v is the addition constant. The other symbols all refer to the pipe width ratio; z indicates whether the width ratio prescribed $\frac{n}{m}$ is to be applied to the octave (13th note, z = 13), eleventh (18th note, z = 18) or other interval, m being the larger, n the smaller figure.

---

125 Theoretisch-praktisches Handbuch der Orgelbaukunst (2nd ed.), Bern, Chur, Leipzig, 1843.

126 If $d_1 < d_x$, both n and m in formula 10 are to be interchanged.

The octave value (d_{13}) of the given pipe in particular (d_1) is:

$$d_{13} = (d_1 - v) \cdot \left(\frac{n}{m}\right)^{\frac{12}{z-1}} + v \qquad (11)$$

The scale ratio, i.e. the octave ratio of widths, is:

$$1 : \left(\frac{m}{n}\right)^{\frac{12}{z-1}} = \left(\frac{n}{m}\right)^{\frac{12}{z-1}} \qquad (12)$$

Here it must be observed that with all scales using addition constants the octave ratio of the so-called basic values (d-v) is implied, not the octave ratio of absolute pipe widths; only the basic values have a constant scale ratio.

Applying these formulae we obtain the following picture in detail:

1. In the medieval scale (see ch.1, part II, above), $v = 0$, $m = n$. Thus in every case $d_x = d_1$, and the scale ratio = 1:1

2. In the old so called constant scale (see chs 2 + 3) $v = 0$, $z = 13$. Thus:

$$\left.\begin{aligned} d_x &= d_1 \cdot \left(\frac{n}{m}\right)^{\frac{x-1}{12}} \\ d_{13} &= d_1 \cdot \frac{n}{m} \end{aligned}\right\} \quad (13)$$

   Alterations in the scale progression are possible on changing the n:m ratio.

3. In the fixed-variable scale with addition constant[127] (see chs 4+5)

$$\left.\begin{aligned} d_x &= (d_1 - v) \cdot \left(\frac{n}{m}\right)^{\frac{x-1}{12}} + v \\ d_{13} &= (d_1 - v) \cdot \frac{n}{m} + v = \frac{d_1 \cdot n + v(m-n)}{m} \end{aligned}\right\} \quad (14)$$

Bedos has n = 1, m = 2, so that the formulae are:

$$\left.\begin{aligned} d_x &= (d_1 - v) \cdot \left(\frac{1}{2}\right)^{\frac{x-1}{12}} + v = \frac{d_1 - v}{\sqrt[12]{2}^{\,(x-1)}} + v \\ d_{13} &= \frac{(d_1 + v)}{2} \end{aligned}\right\} \quad (15)$$

---

[127] Formulae for calculating addition constants may be found on p. 57

In this scaling method, the m:n ratio is constant. The scale's variability is provided by the addition constant v.

4. Sorge's and Töpfer's type of scaling (ch 7) takes v as 0, m = 2, n = 1. Thus:

$$\left.\begin{aligned} d_x &= \frac{d_1}{2^{\frac{x-1}{z-1}}} \\ d_{13} &= \frac{d_1}{2^{\frac{12}{z-1}}} \end{aligned}\right\} \quad (16)$$

By altering the z number, different octave ratios can be obtained with scales of this type.

In Töpfer's "standard scale" (z = 17), these are the values:

$$\left.\begin{aligned} d_x &= \frac{d_1}{2^{\frac{x-1}{16}}} \\ d_{13} &= \frac{d_1}{2^{\frac{12}{16}}} = \frac{d_1}{\sqrt[4]{8}} \end{aligned}\right\} \quad (17)$$

Thus the scale ratio = $1 : \sqrt[4]{8}$

5. Kützing takes 2 standard pipes as basis, the largest d_1 and the smallest d_z. When these values are substituted for m and n, in formula 10, and z = the number of elements from d_1 to d_z ($z > x$ always), the following results are gained:

$$\left.\begin{aligned} d_x &= d_1 \cdot \left(\frac{d_z}{d_1}\right)^{\frac{x-1}{z-1}} = d_z^{\frac{x-1}{z-1}} \cdot d_1^{\frac{z-x}{z-1}} \\ d_{13} &= d_z^{\frac{12}{z-1}} \cdot d_1^{\frac{z-13}{z-1}} \end{aligned}\right\} \quad (18)$$

The scale ratio is $1 : \left(\frac{d_1}{d_z}\right)^{\frac{12}{z-1}}$

9

A few remarks concerning the application of these scaling methods by the old builders in practice may be added here. The basic question is how the various methods affected the elapse of the scale line, more precisely, what form do the departures from standard scale take (using the $1 : \sqrt[4]{8}$ for simplicity) ? To clarify this I will use a type of graphic illustration selected by H. Klotz[128] (see fig. 18). The abscissae represent the elapse of octaves in sequence, the ordinates indicate how many semitones above or below the standard scale or the scale starting point[129], compared with standard scale, the width produced lies. Each line running parallel to the ordinate axis corresponds to the standard scale elapse of $1:\sqrt[4]{8}$.

Drawing in the scales obtained in practice above gives the following

Figure 18 [130]

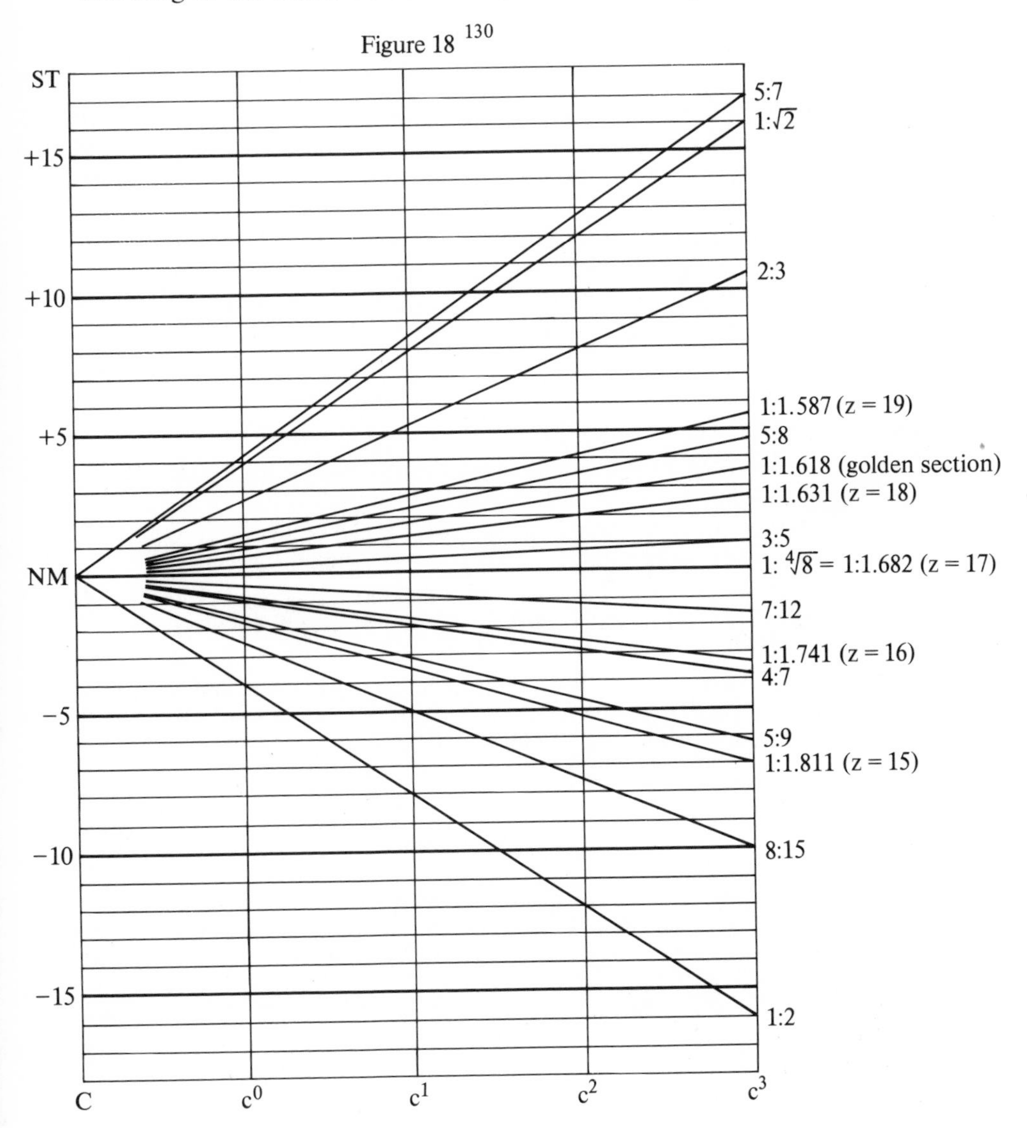

picture a) The scales given in chs 2, 3 and 7 progress as straight lines, making pipe width: standard scale going upwards smaller or larger, depending on what value is given to the n:m ratio or z (fig. 18).
b) The scale with addition constants given in chapter 4 produce lines curving up or down, depending on whether the addition constants are negative or positive. Fig. 19 shows the course of scales provided with positive addition constants, 1:2 (=a), 5:9 (=c), 5:8 (=f), 3:5 (=h), and negative ones: 3:5 (=g), 5:8 (=a), 5:9 (=d), 5:7 (=b). Here the ordinates axis is not fixed, so that it can be placed anywhere, and the starting point of the scale progression set at any given number of semitones above or below the standard scale.[131] All the scale lines show that their inclination depends on the addition constant: pipe width ratio (v:d). From the illustration it can be seen that all scales smaller than the basic 1:8 standard scale (the falling scales in fig. 18) have a low point when a positive addition constant is used, where the scale curve follows standard scale for a while, i.e. forms a horizontal tangent. Thus in the 1:2 scale an absolute low point is always where $v = \frac{d}{4}$. Inversely, all "rising scales", those larger than $1:\sqrt[4]{8}$, have a peak when a negative addition constant is used.[132]

---

[128] Über die Orgelkunst . . . Kassel 1935, p. 188 + 241.

[129] By starting point the intersection between the abscissae of the lowest note, C^0, of a register and the selected scale line is understood.

[130] The illustration shows the scale progression 1:2 previously valid as standard for labials roughly corresponds to the 5:7 scale given as standard for reeds.

[131] The curves are all related in the drawing to the same initial point, since the effect of the different octave ratios and v prefixes are more apparent and it is easier to compare the curves.

[132] Dr Erich Thienhaus, who kindly read through this work in MS, and whom the reader must thank for drawing figures 19 and 20, also brought to my attention the possibility of determining the low or high points by a convenient formula:

$$\left(\frac{v}{d}\right)_{\text{extreme point}} = 1 - \frac{\log \frac{m_a}{n_a}}{\log \frac{m_g}{n_g}} \qquad (19)$$

d = pipe width at high/low point of the scale, v = addition constant, $n_a:m_a$ = standard scale, relative to which the extreme point is to be fixed (i.e., in graphic representation, the scale at the basis of the diagram), $n_g:m_g$ the basic scale of the scale curve to be examined. For $\frac{m_a}{n_a} < \frac{m_g}{n_g}$ v is positive, i.e. to be added to the basic scale values, producing a low. For $\frac{m_a}{n_a} > \frac{m_g}{n_g}$ v becomes negative, thus to be subtracted from the

Figure 19

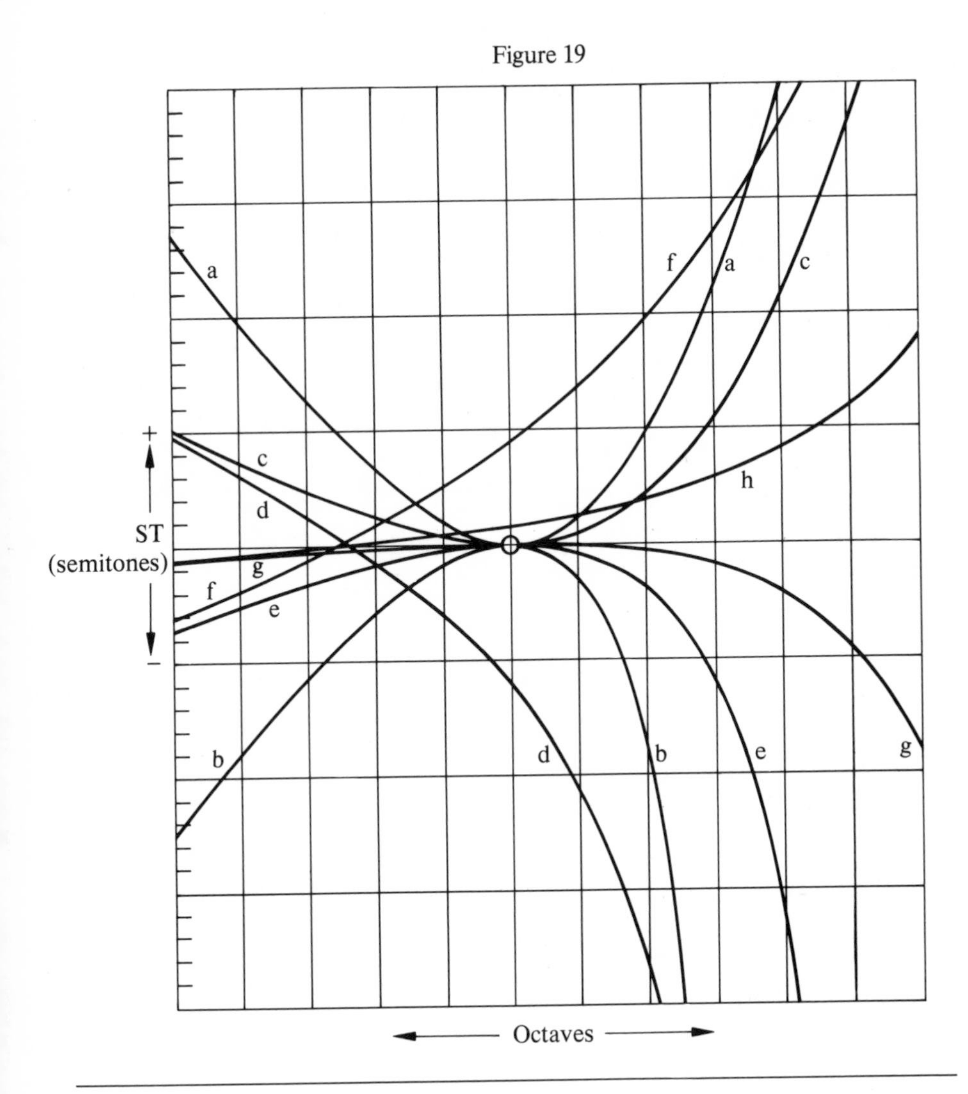

basic scale values, giving a peak. From the development of formula 19 it can also be seen that, where $\frac{m_a}{n_a} > \frac{m_g}{n_g}$ has a positive addition constant, and $\frac{m_a}{n_a} < \frac{m_g}{n_g}$ has a negative one, the scale curves have no extreme point, since here $\frac{v}{d}$ is imaginary. Applying formula 19 the following values are given for the scales shown in fig. 19

$$\left(\frac{m_a}{n_a} = \sqrt[4]{8} \right):$$

see over

c) The scaling forms represented in ch. 5 show an uneven scale curve elapse. In fig. 20 a is the scale given at I on pp 51 and 59, b that at II in fig. 15 on pp 58 and 59, c-g those in fig. 16, p 60. The 2 lower octaves following the 1:2 scale are the same for scales c-g. At h the Bedos 4′ plein jeu scale is given (see p 59 above).

Figure 20

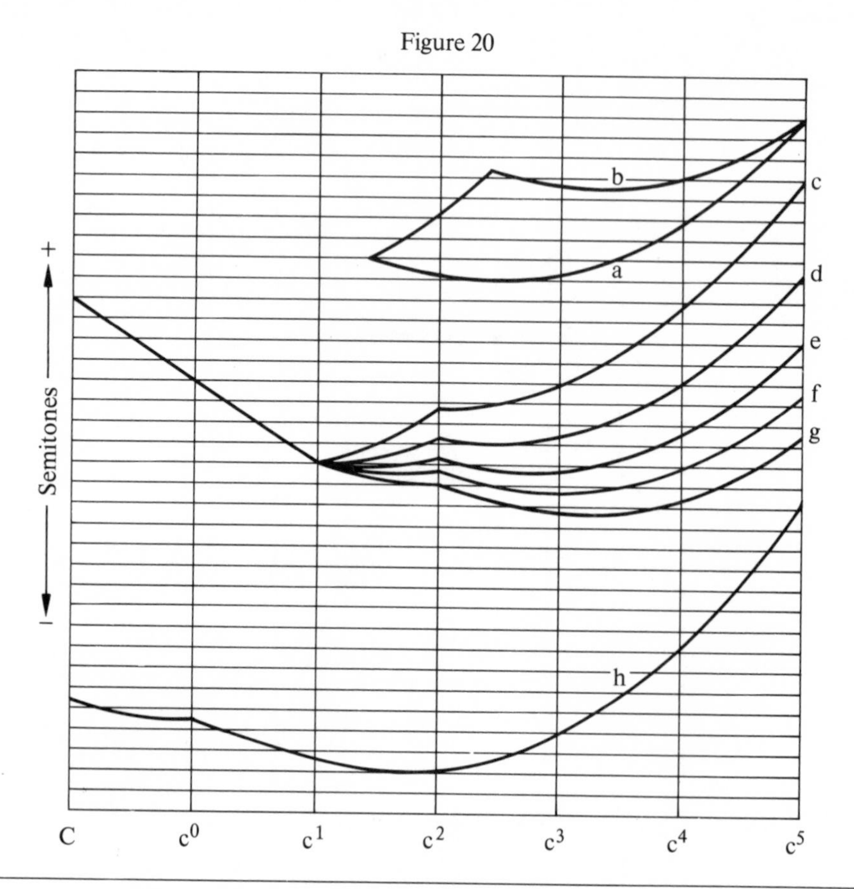

Scale	$\left(\frac{v}{d}\right)$ Extreme point	$\left(\frac{d}{v}\right)$ Extreme point
a = $^1/_2$ + v	0.25	4
b = $^5/_7$ — v	0.545	1.84
c = $^5/_9$ + v	0.116	8.6
e = $^5/_8$ — v	0.0177	56.5
g = $^3/_5$ — v	0.106	9.4

The extreme point is imaginary on the other scale curves.

The following table X may help towards a closer understanding of figure 20.

TABLE X

Curve	Relative value for starting point g	v	Starting point	Position of low point a = above / b = below starting point	$\left(\frac{d}{v}\right)$ Starting point
a)	19	3	f^1	12.9 ST a	7.33
b) 1st branch	8	12	f^1	26 ST b	1.67
2nd "	17	3	f^2	11 ST a	6.67
c) 1st branch	2	2	c^1	19 ST b	2
2nd "	3	1	c^2	±0 ST	4
d) 1st "	3	2	c^1	12 ST b	2.5
2nd "	4	1	c^2	5 ST a	5
e) 1st "	4	2	c^1	7 ST b	3
2nd "	5	1	c^2	8.9 ST a	6
f) 1st "	5	2	c^1	3.5 ST b	3.5
2nd "	6	1	c^2	12 ST a	7
g) 1st "	6	2	c^1	±0 ST	4
2nd "	7	1	c^2	14.7 ST a	8
h) 1st branch	33.83	12.04	C	11 ST b	3.8
2nd "	41.69	4.16	c^0	21 ST a	11.0

For a - g, d and v values are only relative. At h the true width measurements are given. The $\frac{1}{2}$+v octave progression applies to all the curves.

As regards the use of the various scaling methods in practice, the straight-lined scales in this form – at least in baroque organ-building – were less crucial than is normally supposed. The general use of such constant scales as a matter of course has remained true exclusively of the time after A. Sorge. The methods described under b) and c) seem to have been much more frequently used in the earlier period, and certainly they can be demonstrated in a great variety of ways. Let us take the most used 1:2 scale as an example of scaling b) (fig. 19, curve a). Depending on which 4-octave section is chosen, using the old 4-octave compass, the elapse varies. For instance, if the 3rd abscissa from the left is chosen (fig. 19) for C, the 4-octave section shows a first quickly then slowly falling scale, turning upwards in the highest octave.

If the 5th abscissa is chosen as a starting point the scale falls only in the lower octave somewhat, then rises more sharply. Taking abscissa 4 for the C gives an evenly falling then rising scale, with a low at c^1, etc.

The fact that the choice of a (relative to the width of the basic pipe) small addition constant causes the scale first to fall, or to rise if the constant is large, also the fact that the flow point of the 1:2 scale is where $v = \frac{d}{4}$ allowed the old builders to fix the scales at will. An example may clarify this. A 2′ octave is constructed on the 1:2 scale + addition constant as a line 1), first falling then rising in the last 2 octaves, 2) reaching a low at c^0, 3) rising throughout. A "standard rank" constructed on the 3:5 ratio below which the width may not proceed, is taken as given.

The result is shown in table XI (measurements in mm):

TABLE XI

	Key	Normal series 3:5	Scale 1.	Scale 2.	Scale 3.
Low point	—	—	$c^1 = 18$	$c^0 = 30$	$C = 50$
Addition constant	—	—	$v = {}^{18}/_4 = 4.5$	$v = {}^{30}/_4 = 7.5$	$v = {}^{50}/_4 = 12.5$
Basic value at low point	—	—	$c^1 = 18.0 - 4.5 = 13.5$	$c^0 = 30 - 7.5 = 22.5$	$C = 50 - 12.5 = 37.5$
— —	C	50.0	$54.0 + 4.5 = 58.5$	$45.0 + 7.5 = 52.5$	$37.5 + 12.5 = 50.0$
— —	c^0	30.0	$27.0 + 4.5 = 31.5$	$22.5 + 7.5 = 30.0$	$18.8 + 12.5 = 31.3$
— —	c^1	18.0	$13.5 + 4.5 = 18.0$	$11.3 + 7.5 = 18.8$	$9.4 + 12.5 = 21.9$
— —	c^2	10.8	$6.8 + 4.5 = 11.3$	$5.6 + 7.5 = 13.1$	$4.7 + 12.5 = 17.2$
— —	c^3	6.5	$3.4 + 4.5 = 7.9$	$2.8 + 7.5 = 10.3$	$2.3 + 12.5 = 14.8$

So as to be able to fix the low of a scale without difficulty, it was normal to determine the function of a register within a group of specification context. Examining the low points of scales given in Dom Bedos for instance, it can be seen how the starting point[133] (fig. 19) is moved in strict sequence from the narrow low stops via the narrow high ones to the wide high stops gradually to the right, i.e. the low point comes in the highest octave of the 32′ principal ($v = \frac{d}{26}$), but always comes

[133] Cf note 129 above.

earlier in the higher principal ranks (2′octave: $v = \frac{d}{11.1}$). With the wider group stops it is displaced more and more towards the lowest pipe (8′ Gedackt: $v = \frac{d}{6.3}$, tierce $1\frac{3}{5}$′: $v = \frac{d}{8.6}$, larigot $1\frac{1}{3}$′: $v = \frac{d}{6.7}$). Finally, with the quite wide Cornet pipes, the low point is beyond the starting key ($v = \frac{d}{3.6}$ to $\frac{d}{2.8}$), i.e. the scale rises rather quickly from the lowest key.[134] Comparing these, for example, with the diagrams showing Silbermann scales in Klotz[135] (op. cit., p. 241), there is a clear link in the differential treatment of narrow and wide chorus stops, despite any divergence in detail. Closer investigation shows that in fact the basis of baroque scaling lies here; however, to go deeper into this and examine it in depth would exceed the scope of this work.

The same is true of the scale curves under c), which are clearly similar to the lines shown in Klotz, p. 188.[136] Viewed externally this consists only of selecting a new starting point by altering the addition constant once or twice as the scale elapses, or joining a scale line constructed with an addition constant to a straight line scale.

All scales considered hitherto only deal with pipe width. Mouth and cup-up scaling, in the classical age of organ-building, did not generally run parallel to width scale as later. These followed their own rules completely and fall outside the framework of this book.

---

[134] Cf the more detailed discussions on this point in the appendix.

[135] For reasons of space I am unable to give my own diagrams and thus can only refer the reader to Klotz.

[136] H. Klotz gives the C values only from measurements, and the lines joining these points are freely formed. This explains certain departures from my explanation. The main point is whether the old builders generally used scale curves which alter the direction of the bends, as the diagrams in Klotz suggest. If the scale is measured from semitone to semitone in a series of cases, it will be shown that this is a scale bend direction, judged from the C values.

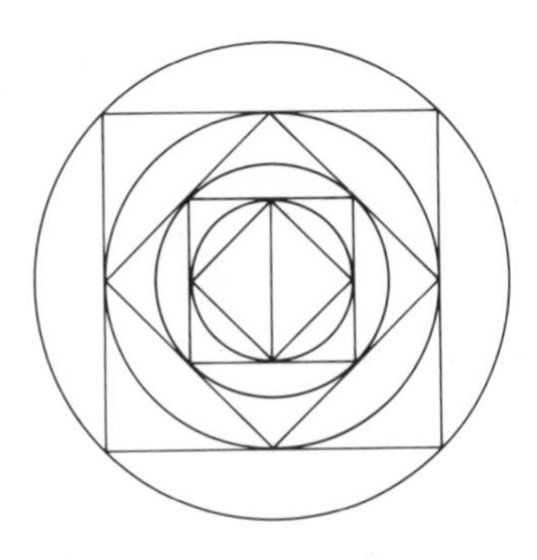

Appendix
The Flue Scales of Dom Bedos

It has already been pointed out several times that this work has had to be restricted for many reasons to demonstrating the various methods of organ scale calculation. However it seems appropriate to show as an appendix, using only one example, how the experience acquired here permits us to obtain the scales of the old builders and to understand their construction laws at a superficial level, as well as to grasp the basis, structure and aims of these scales.

The scales of Bedos are specially suited to be such an example; they have come down to us in written form and thus are known in full detail; they are also easily accessible today.[1]

Until recently the scaling of Bedos has not been particularly highly thought of, if even mentioned at all. For instance, Max Allihn (in J. B. Töpfer, Die Theorie und Praxis des Orgelbaues, 2nd ed., Weimar, 1888, p.278) states: "The scales of Bedos are all variable ones . . . not because he had any particular reason for this, but since he did not know any better. There is no doubt that he would have abandoned his scale if he had known the constant ratio of geometric proportion and had realised that surfaces do not increase in the same ratios as lengths." It is not true that "Bedos did not know the constant ratio of geometric proportion." Almost $1\frac{1}{2}$ centuries before Bedos Mersenne gives instructions for drawing geometric series (see above, p.41). And Bedos himself

---

[1] François Bedos de Celles, L'art du facteur d'orgues, Paris 1766-78, facsimile reprint ed. Christhard Mahrenholz, Bärenreiter, Kassel, 1936.

did not only use the 5:7 octave proportion for reed scales; he also claimed that he was quite able to extend this ratio to smaller key spacings than octaves and make a geometric series with the $1:\sqrt[12]{\frac{7}{5}}^{3}$ ratio[2] (see p. 43 above).

If Bedos did not calculate flue scales using simple geometric proportions (e.g. the 3:5 octave proportion) as Töpfer and Allihn were accustomed to, this may have been for other reasons. Indeed, it does seem that on this point the knowledge and experience of Bedos were far more extensive than his colleagues', who, like Töpfer and Allihn, considered themselves superior to Bedos.

The scaling method of Bedos for flues is, as stated above, the so-called fixed-variable type. The individual scale values are split into a basic value built up in the form of a geometric series on the 1:2 octave ratio, and an addition constant having a positive sign, normally remaining the same within a register, but differing for each register itself.

For greater convenience the flue scales of Bedos are converted into mm and reproduced here giving the true diameter values for all C's[3] .

---

[2] Bedos divides the octave to calculate reed scales in 4 parts, thus bringing every 3 semitones under a common value each.

[3] Bedos give the scale in feet, based on the pied de roi of 324.84mm, inches, = $\frac{1}{12}$', = 27.07mm, lines = $1\frac{1}{12}$' = 2.26mm, and quarters of thirds of lines; the smallest unit of measurement, $\frac{1}{4}$ line, = $\frac{1}{2}$mm, approx. Scale details are given by Bedos according to diameter or pipe circumference, unless, as for all square wooden pipes, the inner or outer pipe depth is given. Naturally certain differences arise between the two sets of details, because Bedos rounds off all values to $\frac{1}{4}$ or $\frac{1}{3}$ lines, so that it may be asked which are original. From the instructions given in the text it seems as if the diameter is the given quantity, from which circumference was calculated (π is taken as 3.14 by Bedos). On the other side there is much that points to circumference as the scaling basis. Thus the diameter of c^3 for Prestant 4', tierce $3\frac{1}{5}$', narrow conical nasard $2\frac{2}{3}$', Quarte 2', Cornet de recit $1\frac{3}{5}$' rank are given as 5''' (11.3mm). For circumference, however, we find these details; for Prestant 4', tierce $3\frac{1}{5}$', Nasard $2\frac{2}{3}$', 1'' $3\frac{3}{4}$''' (35.3mm), for Quarte 2', 1'' 4''' (36.1mm), for Cornet de recit $1\frac{3}{5}$', 1'' $3\frac{1}{2}$''' (35.0mm). It is similar with the Doublette 2' and the narrow Tierce $1\frac{3}{5}$', which both have the same diameter for c^3 ($3\frac{3}{4}$'''), while the circumference of the Doublette is given at $11\frac{3}{4}$''', the tierce at 12'''. It cannot be supposed that Bedos gives the circumference of pipes with the same diameter at 2 or 3 values out of carelessness. It is more likely that in these cases the circumferences represent the first details, whose diameter values coincided with neighbouring values because of rounding off. But since the difference between the two values is everywhere less than $\frac{1}{2}$mm, and in other places the diameter was certainly taken as a starting point, in the following tables I have always taken the diameter values as basis and used the circumference figures to check these. The table figures are all calculated to the 2nd decimal point. The table gives values correct to 1 decimal point. Hence some differences might arise on further calculation.

TABLE I

Register	Basic value g for C key	Addition constant (v)	$\left(\frac{g}{v}\right)$[4] at C	Low point[5] falling on key	True diameter in mm for key C	c⁰	c¹	c²	c³	c⁴
					C	c^0	c^1	c^2	c^3	c^4
1	*2*	*3*	*4*	*5*	*6*	*7*	*8*	*9*	*10*	*11*
Principal 32′	484.5	19.4	25.0	$c\#^2$	503.8	261.6	140.5	79.9	49.6	
Octave 16′	294.4	12.4	23.7	c^2	306.8	159.6	86.0	49.3	30.8	
Octave 8′	143.2	12.5	11.5	b^0	155.7	84.1	48.3	30.4	21.4	
Octave 4′	89.0	5.7	15.6	f^1	94.7	50.2	28.0	16.9	11.3	
Octave 2′	52.3	5.2	10.1	a^0	57.5	31.4	18.3	11.7	8.5	
Open Pedal flute 32′ (wood[6])	463.4	35.6	13.0	$c\#^1$	498.9	267.2	151.4	93.5	64.5	f^3: 57.3
Open Pedal flute 16′ (wood[6])	293.5	29.8	9.9	a^0	323.3	176.5	103.1	66.5	f^2:57.3	
Open Pedal flute 8′ (wood[6])	164.5	26.4	6.2	$c\#^0$	190.9	108.7	67.6	f^1:57.3		
Open Pedal flute 4′ (wood[6])	81.4	26.7	3.0	C	108.2	67.5	f^0:57.3			
Open Pedal fl.4′ metal C-G[7]	90.2	40.6	2.2	G_1	108.3	G:85.7				
Open Pedal fl.4′ met. from G	77.6	8.1	G: 9.6	$d\#^1$	G:85.7	66.3	37.2	22.7		
Bourdon 32′ (wood[6,8])	410.2	27.6	14.9	e^1	437.8	232.7	130.2	78.9		
Bourdon 16′ (wood[6,8])	191.8	32.3	5.9	c^0	224.0	128.1	80.2			
Bourdon 8′ (wood[6,8])	117.1	22.9	5.1	A	140.0	81.5				
Bourdon 4′ / Chimney fl. 4′ wide (metal[8])	71.6	13.1	5.5	$b\flat^0$		84.6	48.8	30.9	22.0[9]	
Bourdon 4′ / Chimney fl. 4′ narrow (metal[8])	61.2	12.1	5.1	a^0		73.3[10]	42.7	27.4	19.7	
Tierce 3 1/5′	89.0	5.7	15.6	f′	94.7	50.2	28.0	16.9	11.3	
Nasard 2 2/3′[11] wide, cylind.	77.6	8.1	9.6	$g\#^0$	85.7	46.9	27.6	17.9	13.0	
Nasard 2 2/3′ narrow, cylind.	63.8	7.9	8.1	f^0	71.6	39.7	23.8	15.8	11.8	
Nasard 2 2/3′ wide, conical, lower	85.4	8.2	10.4	$b\flat^0$	93.6	50.9	29.6	18.9	13.5	
Nasard 2 2/3′ wide, conical, upper	59.2	3.2	1.9	E_1	62.5	32.9	18.1	10.6	6.9	
Nasard 2 2/3′ narrow, conical, lower	64.4	7.3	8.9	g^0	71.6	39.4	23.4	15.3	11.3	
Nasard 2 2/3′ narrow, conical, upper	45.6	2.5	1.8	$D\#_1$	48.1	25.3	13.9	8.2	5.4	
Quarte 2′ wide	65.0	7.2	9.0	g^0	72.2	39.6	23.5	15.3	11.3	
Quarte 2′ narrow[12]	56.2	10.0	5.6	B	66.2	38.1	24.1	17.0	13.5	
Tierce 1 3/5′ wide	52.3	6.9	7.6	e^0	59.2	33.1	20.0	13.4	10.2	
Tierce 1 3/5′ narrow	48.7	5.4	8.9	g^0	54.1	29.8	17.6	11.5	8.5	
Larigot 1 1/3′	40.3	7.1	5.7	B	47.3	27.2	17.1	12.1	9.6	
Plein jeu 4′[13] C-B	67.7	12.0	5.6	B	79.7	45.9				
Plein jeu 4′[13] from c^0	41.7	4.2	10.0	a^1		45.9	25.0	14.6	9.4	6.8
Plein jeu 2′ narrow[14]	37.3	3.3	11.3	b^0		40.6[15]	22.0	12.6	8.0	5.6
Grand Cornet from c^1: 8′[16]	c′:33.8	13.0	c′:2.6	$b\flat^0$			46.8	29.9	21.4	
Grand Cornet from c^1: 4′	c′:28.6	10.9	c′:2.6	$b\flat^0$			39.5	25.2	18.1	
Grand Cornet from c^1: 2 2/3′	c′:21.8	12.0	c′:1.8	$d\#^0$			33.8	22.9	17.5	
Grand Cornet from c^1: 2′	c′:18.8	10.0	c′:1.9	e^0			28.8	19.4	14.7	
Grand Cornet from c^1: 1 3/5′	c′:16.7	7.7	c′:2.1	$f\#^0$			24.3	16.0	11.8	
Cornet de récit from f^0: 8′[16]	f^0:56.8	11.4	f^0:5.0	d^1		f^0:68.2[17]	49.3	30.3	20.9	
Cornet de récit from f^0: 4′	f^0:50.1	8.6	f^0:5.8	f^1		f^0:58.7	42.0	25.3	16.9	
Cornet de récit from f^0: 2 2/3′	f^0:39.3	9.3	f^0:4.2	b^0		f^0:48.5	35.4	22.3	15.8	
Cornet de récit from f^0: 2′	f^0:35.2	7.7	f^0:4.6	c^1		f^0:42.9	31.1	19.4	13.5	
Cornet de récit from f^0: 1 3/5′	f^0:31.1	6.1	f^0:5.1	d^1		f^0:37.2	26.8	16.5	11.3	
Standard flute 4′ (Basse de Viole)	89.0	5.7	15.6	f^1	94.7	50.2	28.0	16.9	11.3	

[4] $\frac{d}{v} = \frac{g}{v} + 1$. E.g., $\frac{g}{v}$ for Principal 32′ = 25.0, $\frac{d}{v}$ = 26.0, etc.

[5] Thus fixing the low point cannot be exact, since the mathematically correct low usually comes at a value between 2 semitones.

[6] For wood pipes Bedos give the inner measurement of the square side. (In the scale representation found in my "Die neue Marien-Orgel in Göttingen", the square side value has been wrongly given as pipe diameter.) to convert wood pipes with square side a into circular metal pipes with diameter d Bedos makes $a = d - \frac{1}{9}d$, hence $d = \frac{9}{8}.a$. I have calculated the table figures using the formula $d = \frac{2a}{\sqrt{\pi}}$

[7] For the metal flute 4′ in the Pedal, Bedos gives the wide cylindrical Nasard scale, thus starting it as a 4′ rank with G^0. For the absent C^0-F♯^{0} pipes Bedos suggests a scale line beginning at C^0 with 4″ (108.3 mm = C^0 diameter of the wood Pedal flute 4′), going into the wide cylindrical Nasard scale (85.7mm).

[8] In the Bourdons Bedos differentiates between treble and bass. Amongst the latter he includes the areas of the 32′, 16′ and 8′ stopped ranks up to 4′ C. The continuation is provided always by metal pipes, stopped or chimneyed, which all belong to the trebles.

[9] The circumference of pipe c^3 of the Bourdon 4′ and chimney flute 4′ is given by Bedos both in the chart description (p.66f) and the scale table (p.77) at 1″6½‴ (41.7mm), whilst the diameter value is to be 9¾″ (22.0mm). The circumference should probably be 2″6½‴ (68.8mm).

[10] The diameter of the narrow Bourdon 4′ and chimney flute 4′ should be 8½‴ for C 2′ (73.3mm); the circumference is too large for this at 8″8‴.

[11] Quint 5⅓′ is so constructed by Bedos that one of the 4 2⅔′ scales offered is chosen for the three upper octaves and the lower octave is formed from suitably scaled Bourdon or open Pedal flute pipes.

[12] The narrow Quarte 2′ scale is especially surprising because the value of its c^3 goes beyond that of the wide Quarte. Thus both scale lines cut. But on Bedos' scale chart the narrow Quarte is so drawn that in all regions it remains under the values of the wide Quarte. However, as the same figures are presented in the scale description (p.66) as in the chart (p.77), taking the c^3 value of the narrow Quarte wider than that of the wide Quarte, it must be assumed that the drawing is incorrect.

[13] On the Plein jeu scale cf above p. 59 and 72.

[14] The narrow Plein jeu scale is not drawn in on the charts in Bedos. It is added on p.476 of his work, and thus not considered in the examinations of Bedos' scales hitherto.

[15] The C 2′ circumference of the narrow Plein jeu is wrongly given as 2″1½‴ (57.5mm), whilst the diameter would have to be 128mm approx, with the given diameter of 1″6‴= 40.6mm. The diameter value given is the right one.

[16] The 8′ ranks of the two Cornets are chimney flutes. The chimneys have ¼ the body width as diameter and half the body length.

[17] The diameter of f^0 of the 8′ Cornet de recit rank is given in the table at 2″6‴, in the text as 2″6¼‴. The last value, as checking from pipe circumference shows (7″11‴), is the right one.

(These scales have already been published in my "Die neue Marienorgel zu Göttingen," 1st ed., Göttingen and Kassel, 1926. Some errors there are corrected in this work.)

The basic values given in column 2 of table I, it becomes clear on closer inspection, are bigger in registers of the same family (compared to a standard scale constructed according to $1:\sqrt[4]{8}$) the lower the stop concerned. Likewise the addition constant (column 3) is largest, apart from certain divergences, in stops with large foot lengths (32′, 16′, etc.), becoming smaller the lower the foot length.

Columns 4 and 5 in table I give an interpretation of these phenomena just mentioned. Here it becomes clear that the variances in scale line development indicated are caused by the variances in value $(\frac{g}{v})_{C^0}$[18] and also with the different positioning of the low points stretched out over 4 octaves, between the keys $D\sharp_1$[19] and $c\sharp^2$. For convenience the following table II gives the low points in the key order series and breaks up all the registers shown by Bedos into families.

From table II it can be seen that in all the register families the low point is displaced upwards if the foot length is large. Thus with Principal 32′ and 16′ for 3 octaves the scale falls, compared with the standard 1: 8 scale, until it has reached the low at keys c^2 or $c\sharp^2$ and slowly moves up again in the uppermost octave. By contrast Octave 2′ has its low at a^0; it rises in the elapse of the second octave, and achieves relatively large widths in the high regions. It is just the same for Pedal flutes, Bourdons[20] and nearly all the aliquots.

When this is taken together with the statement above that the basic values (compared to standard scale $1:\sqrt[4]{8}$) always become larger the lower the pipe rank is, respecting its foot length, we arrive at the fundamental scaling law (also given as theory on p. 69 of Bedos' work): with two pipes of the same height from different registers, the one lower on the keyboards must be the wider. Or, put another way; the higher

---

[18] The $(\frac{g}{v})$ value in Bedos varies between 1.8 and 25.0. With Bendeler's scale recorded above, constructed according to the same principles, having a standard pipe width of 35 scruples and a lower octave pipe width of 70 scruples less 5-10 scruples, the distance between $(\frac{g}{v})$ values at C^0 is considerably less; the values are 4.2 and 10.4. The lows are between $F\sharp^0$ and $b\flat^0$, and thus do not go beyond the centre of the keyboard.

[19] The keys $D\sharp_1$-B_1 are only imagined; they are given because the low of some stops is below the lower limit of the keyboard; these scales concerned thus beginning at the bottom of the keyboard are rising scales. It is similar for the Grand Cornet, which begins at c^1, but has imagined low points before.

[20] The 4′ Bourdons cannot be considered independent stops; see above and below, notes 8 and 21.

TABLE II

Low point at	Principals	Pedal flutes	Bourdons	Aliquots	Grand Cornet	Cornet de Récit
D♯$_1$ [19]				con. Nasard 2 2/3′ narrow [21]		
E$_1$				con. Nasard 2 2/3′ wide [21]		
F$_1$						
F♯$_1$						
G$_1$		4′ Metal C-G				
G♯$_1$						
A$_1$						
B♭$_1$						
B$_1$						
C		4′ Wood				
C♯						
D						
D♯						
E						
F						
F♯						
G						
G♯						
A			Bourdon 8′			
B♭						
B	Plein jeu 4′ wide C-B			{ Quarte 2′ narrow		
c			Bourdon 16′	{ Larigot 1 1/3′		
c♯		8′ Wood				
d						
d♯					2 2/3′	
e				Tierce 1 3/5′ wide	2′	
f				cylind. Nasard 2 2/3′ narrow		
f♯					1 3/5′	
g				{ con. Nasard 2 2/3′ narr. below { Tierce 1 3/5′ narrow { Quarte 2′ wide		
g♯			(22	cylind. Nasard 2 2/3′ wide		
a	Octave 2′	16′ Wood	Bourdon 4′ nar.			
b♭			Bourdon 4′ wid.	con. Nasard 2 2/3′ wide below	{ 8′	
b	{ Plein jeu 2′ narrow { Octave 8′				{ 4′	2 2/3
c^1						2′
c♯^{1}		32′ Wood				
d^1						{ 1 3/5′ { 8′
d♯^{1}		4′ Metal (from G)				
e^1			Bourdon 32′			
f^1	{ Octave 4′ { Basse de Viole 4′			Tierce 3 1/5′		4′
f♯^{1}						
g^1						
g♯^{1}						
a^1	Plein jeu 4′ wide from c					
b♭^{1}						
b^1						
c^2	Octave 16′					
c♯^{2}	Principal 32′					

octave rank of a register family always starts narrower than the lower octave rank, compared to standard scale. Balance is created by the low point of the lower octave rank's being higher on the keyboard; thus this octave rank "falls" for longer (declines, compared with the standard scale), while the higher octave rank, which is narrower at its starting point, has an earlier low point and this rises more quickly in width.

Here it must be observed that, as table II clearly shows, the Principal group, including mixtures, reaches its low relatively late, in contrast to the other register families, which form distinct narrow and wide groups, as far as they are separate from the Principal group. Further the two Cornets differ sharply from the Principal series, seeing that the Grand Cornet starts at c^1, the Cornet de récit at f^0, so that the low for the Grand Cornet is below the beginning of the stop; thus the register mounts steeply in scale from its start and reaches a relatively larger width in the upper regions than the Cornet de récit, whose lows are almost an octave higher.

It should not be overlooked that the Principals, as regards rank sequence, have the order 32′, 16′, 8′, 4′, 2′, and that both Cornets concur in their low points, from above downwards, with a sequence of 4′, 8′, $1\frac{3}{5}$′, 2′, $2\frac{2}{3}$′, so that $2\frac{2}{3}$′ going upwards has the sharpest incline relatively, the 4′ the smallest, reversed with the individual aliquots, where the elapse of the low positions is the same as for Principals, Pedal flutes and Bourdons ($3\frac{1}{5}$′, $2\frac{2}{3}$′, 2′, $1\frac{3}{5}$′, $1\frac{1}{3}$′,). Both conical nasards have a low 2 semitones above the corresponding cylindrical quint stops.

When a wide and a narrow scale is offered for a register, the narrow scale has low point always 2-4 semitones earlier[23], which favours the stop's width in the high regions. With the tierce $1\frac{3}{5}$′ this situation is reversed; the low of the narrow tierce is 3 semitones higher than that of the wide tierce.

Table II presented the low point position of the Bedos scales in the context of the keyboard assumed by him (C-d^3), while table III arranges the lows according to the absolute pitch of the notes con-

---

[21] The upper widths of the conical Nasard are given here as individual ranks, although they cannot be considered as independent stops. From the unusually early position of the low it can be seen that the upper width of the conical nasards rise sharply upwards and thus the ratio between upper and lower widths becomes smaller continually.

[22] Bourdon 4′, narrow and wide, is intended by Bedos as a continuation of the 32′, 16′ and 8′ series upwards (see note 8). A start at c^0 is supposed. For an independent 4′ rank beginning at C^0, the lows would be between $B\flat^0$ and B^0.

[23] As much as 8 semitones with the Quarte 2′, with the result that the narrow Quarte scale at the top goes above the wide scale (see above note 12).

TABLE III

Lowpoint position related to 8′ rank	Principals and Mixtures	Open Pedal flutes	Bourdons	Aliquots	Grand Cornet	Cornet de Récit
C			Bourdon 16′			
C♯		Pedal flute 32′				
D						
D♯						
E			Bourdon 32′			
F						
F♯						
G		Metal flute 4′ C-G				
G♯						
A		Pedal flute 16′	Bourdon 8′	con. Nasard 2 2/3′ narrow		
B♭						
B				con. Nasard 2 2/3′ wide		
c		Wood flute 4′				
c♯	Principal 32′	Pedal flute 8′				
d						
d♯						
e						
f						
f♯						
g						
g♯						
a			Bourdon 4′ nar.			
b♭			Bourdon 4′ wid.		8′	
b	{ Plein jeu 4′ C-B Octave 8′					
c¹	Octave 16′					
c♯¹						
d¹						8′
d♯¹						
e¹						
f¹						
f♯¹						
g¹						
g♯¹						
a¹						
b♭¹						
b¹					{ 4′ 2 2/3′	
c²				Quarte 2′ narrow		
c♯²				cylind. Nasard 2 2/3′ narrow		
d²						
d♯²				conical Nasard 2 2/3′ narrow		
e²		Metal flute 4′ from G		cylind. Nasard 2 2/3′ wide		
f²	{ Octave 4′ Basse de Viole 4′				2′	4′
f♯²				conical Nasard 2 2/3′ wide		
g²				Larigot 1 1/3′		2 2/3′
g♯²				Quarte 2′ wide		
a²	{ Plein jeu 4′ from c Octave 2′			Tierce 1 3/5′ wide		
b♭²				Tierce 3 1/5′		
b²					1 3/5′	
c³				Tierce 1 3/5′ narrow		
c♯³	Plein jeu 2′ narrow					2′
d³						
d♯³						
e³						
f³						
f♯³						1 3/5′

cerned, i.e. related to the 8′ pitch.

From table III it can be seen more clearly than table II that the aliquots form the natural continuation of the Bourdon family and a closed group with it, standing independently, next to the Principal and Mixture group. Apart from the metal Pedal flute 4′ given by Bedos only for information, the Pedal flutes appear collected together at a particular low position and thus fulfilling a particular function. It is noteworthy here too, as in table II, that the arrangement of octave ranks shows a certain inversion:

Bourdons: 16′, 32′, 8′, (4′)
Principals: 32′, 8′, 16′, 4′, 2′
Wood Pedal flutes: 32′, 16′, 4′, 8′

With the aliquots first the narrow ranks begin (except for the tierce, see above), then the wide ranks.

Both Cornets clearly show their nevertheless unified structured progression. The low points of the $2\frac{2}{3}$′, 2′ and $1\frac{3}{5}$′ choruses in both Cornets are 6 semitones apart; the Cornet de récit has lows 8 semitones higher than the Grand Cornet. The structure of the 8′ and 4′ ranks evolves in the same way for both Cornets.

In conclusion it will be attempted to bring the various Bedos scales into a comparative relationship with standard $1 : \sqrt[4]{8}$ scale. This cannot be done, for instance, by calculating all the values produced for C^0 or the C 2′ note and determining their divergence from standard scale, since the basis of comparison – as is in the essence of the fixed variable scale – will have altered a few notes above or below. A suitable basis for comparison can probably only be established by determining the departure from standard scale at the scale low point, i.e. the size of the ordinate (see fig. 19) is determined at the low point, and thus the position of the scale curve in the coordinate region. Table IV gives the result of such a deliberation. For greater exactness semitones are further divided into quarter tones.

Table IV shows that, at the low point, Principals are all $1\frac{1}{2}$–3 semitones below standard scale, i.e. always have the same basis point for scale calculation. It is similar for Bourdons (2-4 semitones under standard measurements)[24] and Pedal flutes (2-3 semitones above standard scale), of which – apart from the 7 lowest notes of the metal flute 4′ – only the 32′ Pedal flute is scaled differently, 3 semitones downwards. The narrow aliquots are all $2\frac{1}{2}$–4 semitones below the same stops with wide scale; only the Quarte 2′ is an exception, in as far as both the

[24] Only the narrow Bourdon 4′ goes as far as 6 semitones below standard scale.

TABLE IV

Departure from standard scale 1 : $\sqrt[4]{8}$ for lowpoint in semitones	Principals and Mixtures	Open Pedal flutes	Bourdons	Aliquots	Grand Cornet	Cornet de Récit
+ 11						1⅗′
10½						2′
10						
9½						
9					1⅗′	2⅔′
8½					2′	
8		Metal flute 4′ C-G				
7½						
7					2⅔′	
6½						
6						
5½						
5					4′	4′
4½						
4				Quarte 2′ wide and narrow		
3½				Tierce 1 3/5′ wide		
3		Pedal flute 16′ Pedal flute 4′ Metal flute 4′ from G		Larigot 1 1/3′ cylind. Nasard 2 2/3′ wide		
2½				conical Nasard 2 2/3′ wide		
2 semitones		Pedal flute 8′				
1½						
1 semitone				Tierce 1 3/5′ narrow		
+ ½				Tierce 3 1/5′		
− ½				conical Nasard 2 2/3′ narrow		
1 semitone		Pedal flute 32′		cylind. Nasard 2 2/3′ narrow		
1½	Octave 2′					
2 semitones			Bourdon 8′			
2½	Octave 16′					8′
3	Principal 32′ Octave 8′ and 4′ Basse de Viole 4′		Bourdon 4′ wide			
3½					8′	
4	Plein jeu 4′ C-B		Bourdon 32′+16′			
4½						
5						
5½						
6	Plein jeu 4′ from c		Bourdon 4′ narr.			
6½						
7						
7½						
8						
8½						
− 9	Plein jeu 2′ narrow					

narrow and wide Quartes have the same ordinate at the low point (4 semitones above standard scale); the difference between the two stops comes from the differing position of the starting point, their curves being otherwise the same. Concerning the rank sequence of widths in the aliquots; the $1\frac{3}{5}'$ and $1\frac{1}{3}'$ follow the 2′ as the widest stop, then the cylindrical and conical nasard $2\frac{2}{3}'$ (i.e. the tierce $1\frac{3}{5}'$ is wider scaled than the Quinte $2\frac{2}{3}'$). The $3\frac{1}{5}'$ is kept relatively narrow (as with the narrow tierce $1\frac{3}{5}'$). In table IV the division by groups is again prominent. The Principal and mixture group, whose widths are all under standard scale, are on one side, the group of Bourdons and aliquots, nearly all wider than standard,[25] on the other.

Whilst the register groups examined up till now have been collected together round a common low point, the two Cornets have lows spread apart, suggesting that the individual Cornet choruses have special functions to fulfill. Parallelism in the Cornet structure is also seen elsewhere, in both the width order is $1\frac{3}{5}'$, 2′, $2\frac{2}{3}'$, 4′, 8′ (thus the highest choruses are the widest, the reverse of the Principals, where the high mixtures have the narrowest ranks), in both the $1\frac{3}{5}'$ and 2′ are a quarter tone, the 2′ and $2\frac{2}{3}'$ $1\frac{1}{2}$ semitones apart. These three choruses are scaled 2 semitones wider in the Cornet de récit than the Grand Cornet; here is the balance to the very early Grand Cornet low point seen in table II, where all the choruses automatically attain larger widths at the top.[26] This examination, which had to remain sketchy for reasons of space, has surely proved sufficiently that the flue scaling of Bedos is based on a thoroughly worked out plan, and that the values given by him are not the chance results of organ-building practice; they represent quantities taking all details into account and blending into a total concept.

---

[25] The reason for the fact that the Bourdons do not apparently follow this principle is that, in accordance with modern usage, the details in table IV are based on a comparison with a standard scale stopped rank of the same pitch. The Bourdons cannot be related to open pipes of the same pitch without qualification; they really correspond to open pipes with considerably greater body width. In this connexion the method of various early theorists of seeking a comparison basis for stopped pipes in pipes of the same body length, is worthy of notice. In this case that would mean Bourdon 8′ could be compared at +10 semitones, Bourdon 4′ at +9, Bourdon 32′ and 16′ at +8, Bourdon 4′ (narrow) at +6. The stopped ranks then give way quite naturally to the aliquots.

[26] Bedos gives an explanation for the differential scaling of the two Cornets mentioned here and previously, on p. 71 of his work.

DORDT COLLEGE LIBRARY
Sioux Center, Iowa 51250